REVISE AQA GCSE (9–1)
Physics
REVISION WORKBOOK
Foundation

Series Consultant: Harry Smith

Author: Catherine Wilson

Also available to support your revision:

The **Revise GCSE Study Skills Guide** is full of tried-and-trusted hints and tips for how to learn more effectively. It gives you techniques to help you achieve your best – throughout your GCSE studies and beyond!

The **Revise GCSE Revision Planner** helps you to plan and organise your time, step-by-step, throughout your GCSE revision. Use this book and wall chart to mastermind your revision.

For the full range of Pearson revision titles across KS2, KS3, GCSE, Functional Skills, AS/A Level and BTEC visit:
www.pearsonschools.co.uk/revise

Question difficulty
Look at this scale next to each exam-style question. It tells you how difficult the question is.

Contents

AQA publishes Sample Assessment Material and the Specification on its website. This is the official content and this book should be used in conjunction with it. The questions have been written to help you practise every topic in the book. Remember: the real exam questions may not look like this.

Energy stores and systems

1 Identify which of the following is an energy store.

Tick **one** box.

wind ☐

light ☐

radiation ☐

elastic potential ☐

(1 mark)

2 Identify the correct energy stores that occur in the following examples by drawing lines to show your answers. The first one has been done for you.

A	A container box lifted by a crane
B	Hot water in a saucepan
C	Bag of coal
D	Moving wind turbine

| chemical |
| gravitational |
| kinetic |
| thermal |

(1 mark)

3 The principle of the conservation of energy states that energy can be usefully transferred to other stores. Complete the energy flow diagram below to show the changes in energy stores and transfers for a battery-operated music system, when it is switched on. Write the correct description of energy in each box.

> Your answer should include the following terms: 'electrical current', 'heating', 'chemical energy', 'sound'.

(a) Store of ....

....

....

→

(b) Energy transfer by

....

....

→

(c) Energy transfer to

....

....

(3 marks)

4 A basket of apples is lowered to the ground from an apple tree using a rope and pulley. The total energy transferred is 250 J. Describe the energy transfers taking place, including the useful and wasteful energy components that result.

....

....

....

....

....

....

.... **(4 marks)**

1

Changes in energy

1   Choose the correct equation for calculating gravitational potential energy.

> Always answer multiple-choice questions, even if you don't actually know the answer.

Tick **one** box.

$E_p = m\,v\,h$ ☐ $E_p = m\,F\,a$ ☐

$E_p = \frac{1}{2}\,m\,v^2$ ☐ $E_p = m\,g\,h$ ☐   **(1 mark)**

2   A cyclist and her bicycle are travelling at 6 m/s.

> Guided

The mass of the cyclist and bicycle is 70 kg.

Calculate the kinetic energy of the cyclist. Choose the correct unit from the box.

m/s^2	J	W

Kinetic energy = ...

so ....

Kinetic energy = ... unit .... **(3 marks)**

3   A spring has a spring constant of 200 N/m.

It is stretched 15 cm when a mass is applied.

Calculate the energy transferred to the spring. Use the correct equation from the Physics Equation Sheet.

....

....

Energy transferred = ... J **(3 marks)**

4   A dancer with a mass of 60 kg practises chin-ups during training and raises her body 0.7 m.

Calculate the gravitational potential energy gained by the dancer between the bottom and top of the chin-up.

> Use g = 10 N/kg in the equation that links m, g and h.

....

....

Gravitational potential energy = ... J **(2 marks)**

Energy changes in systems

1 Give the equation for specific heat capacity.

.... **(1 mark)**

2 Calculate how much energy is needed to heat 0.8 kg of water from 30 °C to 80 °C. The specific heat capacity of water is 4200 J/kg °C. Use the correct equation from the Physics Equation Sheet.

....

....

....

Energy required = ... J   **(3 marks)**

Guided

3 A 1.2 kg block of copper is supplied with 20 000 J of electrical energy. Calculate the change in temperature of the copper. The specific heat capacity of copper is 385 J/kg °C. Use the correct equation from the Physics Equation Sheet.

> You will need to rearrange the equation you used in Question 2.

$\Delta\theta = \dfrac{\Delta E}{(m\ c)}$, so $\Delta\theta = \dfrac{20\,000}{\text{..........................}}$

....

....

Change in temperature of the copper = ... °C   **(3 marks)**

4 A metal block of mass 0.8 kg is connected to a heater which transfers 16 200 J of energy to the block. The temperature increase is 25 °C. Calculate the specific heat capacity of the block of metal. Use the correct equation from the Physics Equation Sheet.

....

....

....

....

Specific heat capacity = ... J/kg °C   **(3 marks)**

Practical skills

Required practical –
Specific heat capacity

1 Water is widely used in cooling systems because of its relatively high specific heat capacity compared with some other liquids.

(a) Write the definition of the term 'specific heat capacity'.

.... **(1 mark)**

(b) Give the three quantities that need to be measured to calculate the specific heat capacity of a substance.

.... **(1 mark)**

2 (a) Describe an experiment that could be set up to measure the specific heat capacity of water using an electric water heater, a beaker and a thermometer.

> Remember 'pre-experiment' steps, e.g. zero the balance to eliminate the mass of apparatus before measuring substances, take a starting temperature reading before heating and decide on the range or type of measurements to be taken.

....

....

....

....

....

....

....

.... **(5 marks)**

(b) Suggest how you can determine the amount of thermal energy supplied to the heater by the electric current.

....

....

.... **(2 marks)**

(c) Describe how this experiment could be improved to give more accurate results.

....

....

.... **(2 marks)**

3 A known mass of ice is heated until it becomes steam. The temperature is recorded every minute. Describe how to use the data to identify when there are changes of state.

....

....

.... **(2 marks)**

Power

1 A kettle transfers 12 500 J of electrical energy in 5 seconds. What is the power rating of the kettle?

Tick **one** box.

2500 W ☐   25 000 W ☐

12 500 W ☐   62 500 W ☐   **(1 mark)**

2 A microwave heats a drink in 20 seconds using 15 000 J of electrical energy. Calculate the power of the microwave.

Energy transferred = ... J, time taken = ... s

$P = \frac{E}{t} =$ .... W

Power = ... W   **(2 marks)**

3 A student with a mass of 60 kg climbs 20 stairs to a physics lab. Each stair is 0.08 m high; g is 10 N/kg.

(a) Calculate the gravitational potential energy gained in climbing the 20 stairs to the lab.
    Select the correct unit from the box.

watts	newtons	joules

You need to remember that $E_p = m\,g\,h$ because it's not on the Physics Equation Sheet.

....

....

Gravitational potential energy = ... unit .... **(3 marks)**

(b) Calculate the power of the student's muscles to climb the stairs in 12 seconds.
    Include the unit in your answer.

....

Power = ... **(1 mark)**

4 Two students investigate the time taken for two different winch motors to transfer energy.

You will need to recall the equation $P = E / t$

(a) Calculate the time taken for a 3 W winch motor to transfer 360 J of energy.

....

.... **(2 marks)**

(b) Calculate the time taken for a 5 W winch motor to transfer 360 J of energy.

....

.... **(2 marks)**

Energy transfers and efficiency

1 (a) Identify the most suitable material, from the table below, for building an energy efficient garage.

Material	Relative thermal conductivity
brick	1.06
concrete	1.00
sandstone	2.20
granite	2.75

.... **(1 mark)**

(b) Define the term 'low relative thermal conductivity' of a material.

....

.... **(2 marks)**

2 (a) Some houses are built with very thick walls. Explain how these walls help to keep the houses warm in the winter.

> Guided

Thicker walls provide more material for ....

to travel through from the inside to outside, so the ....

.... is less, keeping the houses warmer.   **(2 marks)**

(b) In hot countries, some traditional houses have thick walls with small windows. Explain why.

Thicker walls provide more material for ....

to travel through from the outside to inside, so the ....

.... is less, keeping the houses cool. **(2 marks)**

3 A student uses four beakers containing hot water, each wrapped with different insulating materials, to investigate the transfer of thermal energy. Which factor will **not** affect the rate of transfer of thermal energy?

Tick **one** box.

rate of data collection ☐ temperature of the room ☐

starting temperature of water ☐ thickness of the insulators ☐ **(1 mark)**

4 A box gains 100 J of energy in its gravitational potential energy store when it is lifted from the floor to a lab desk. The motor lifting the box transfers 400 J as kinetic energy.

> Remember: efficiency = $\dfrac{\text{useful energy transferred by the machine}}{\text{total energy supplied to the machine}}$

Calculate the efficiency of the motor.

....

....

.... **(2 marks)**

Practical skills

Required practical – Thermal insulation

1 (a) Describe an experimental method, using the apparatus in the diagram below, to investigate the insulating properties of different materials.

thermometer — polystyrene — cardboard

beaker — 250cm³ — 4:48 — bubblewrap

water — stopwatch

....

....

....

....

....

....

....

.... **(5 marks)**

(b) Identify the independent and dependent variables in this experiment.

....

.... **(2 marks)**

(c) Name **four** control variables in this experiment.

....

....

.... **(2 marks)**

2 Identify a hazard with conducting this experiment and explain how the risks to those conducting the experiment may be minimised.

....

.... **(1 mark)**

3 Suggest an alternative piece of apparatus **not** shown in the diagram that could be used for data collection to improve accuracy.

.... **(1 mark)**

4 Describe the conclusion that you would expect to reach at the end of the experiment which relates the independent and dependent variables.

....

....

.... **(2 marks)**

Energy resources

1   Name **three** non-renewable energy resources.

   1. ....

   2. ....

   3. ....   **(1 mark)**

2   A hydroelectric power station is used to produce electricity when demand is high.

   (a)   Explain why the hydroelectric power station is a reliable producer of electricity.

   > Hydroelectric power relies on water power; you need to explain why this is reliable.

   ....

   ....

   ....

   ....   **(2 marks)**

   (b)   Give **one** reason why we cannot use hydroelectric power stations in more places in the UK.

   ....

   ....   **(1 mark)**

3   For each of the following statements about fossil fuels, describe the negative environmental impacts.

   > Think about the possible consequences of the statements describing the use of fossil fuels.

   (a)   Carbon dioxide is released as a result of burning fossil fuels.

   ....

   ....

   ....   **(2 marks)**

   (b)   Burning fossil fuels produces sulfur dioxide and nitrogen oxides.

   ....

   ....

   ....   **(2 marks)**

   (c)   Fossil fuels need to be extracted from the ground and transported to the power station.

   ....

   ....

   ....   **(2 marks)**

Patterns of energy use

1 The graphs show patterns of energy use and human population growth.

(a) Give **three** reasons why energy consumption rose significantly after the year 1900.

1. After 1900, the world's energy demand .... as the population grew.

2. There was development in ....

3. The rise of power stations using fossil fuels added to .... **(3 marks)**

(b) (i) Identify the **three** main energy resources used to provide the world's energy between the years 1000 and 2000.

.... **(1 mark)**

(ii) Suggest **two** reasons why the use of energy resources has increased in the developed world.

1. ....

2. .... **(2 marks)**

(iii) Suggest why nuclear energy resources appear only after 1950.

.... **(1 mark)**

(iv) Identify a renewable resource from the graph that makes use of gravitational potential energy.

.... **(1 mark)**

2 In the graph in question 1, the patterns in energy consumption are similar to the pattern in the world's population growth. Describe the issues that may result from the continuing use of energy in the future, at the same rate as shown in the graph.

Consider the finite resources and increasing demand.

....
....
....
....
....
.... **(4 marks)**

9

Extended response – Energy

A girl plays on a swing in the park. The swing seat is initially pulled back by her friend to 30° to the vertical position and then released. Describe the energy changes in the motion of the swing as it swings backwards and forwards.

Your answer should also explain, in terms of energy, why the swing eventually stops.

> You will be more successful in extended response questions if you plan your answer before you start writing.
>
> The question asks you to give a detailed explanation of the energy changes as the swing moves backwards and forwards. Think about:
>
> - how gravitational potential energy changes as the swing is pulled back
> - points where gravitational potential energy (E_p) and kinetic energy (E_k) are at maximum and at 0
> - where some energy may be lost from the system
> - why the swing will eventually stop.
>
> You should try to use the information given in the question.

....

....

....

....

....

....

....

....

....

....

....

....

....

.... **(6 marks)**

Circuit symbols

1 Select the component that is designed to respond to changes in levels of light.

Tick **one** box.

diode   ☐

LED   ☐

LDR   ☐

thermistor   ☐

(1 mark)

2 (a) The three symbols below represent three components. Write the name of each component in the corresponding box.

1	2	3

(3 marks)

   (b) Identify which component in (a) is commonly found in a household plug connected to the live wire.

.... **(1 mark)**

3 Complete the table of circuit symbols below:

Component	Symbol	Purpose
ammeter		
		provides a fixed resistance to the flow of current
	▷├	
		allows the current to be switched on / off

(4 marks)

4 Draw a circuit that could be used to measure the resistance of an unknown resistor.

> Consider whether each component should be connected in series or in parallel.

(4 marks)   **11**

Electrical charge and current

1   The electric current flowing in a circuit is 4 A.

(a)   Explain what is meant by an electric current.

....

.... **(2 marks)**

(b)   The current flows for 8 seconds. Calculate how much charge has flowed.

Choose the correct unit from the box.

C   J   A

> You need to recall the equation:
> charge flow = current × time ($Q = I\,t$)

....

....

Charge = ... unit................... **(3 marks)**

2   The diagram shows a series circuit.

0.3 A

(a)   (i)   Explain why the readings on ammeter 1 and ammeter 3 would both be 0.3 A.

.... **(1 mark)**

(ii)   Describe how you could increase the size of the current flowing through the circuit.

.... **(1 mark)**

(b)   Identify the component in the circuit that enables the electrical charge to flow.

> For an electrical charge to flow, the circuit must include a source of potential difference.

.... **(1 mark)**

3   A student is investigating how current carries electrical charge round the circuit.

(a)   Draw a circuit diagram to show how the electrical charge could be measured.

Guided

(2 marks)

(b)   Give **one** other piece of equipment the student would need to calculate electrical charge.

.... **(1 mark)**

Current, resistance and pd

1   Choose the quantity that the ohm (Ω) is the unit of.

Tick **one** box.

current ☐   potential difference ☐

energy ☐   resistance ☐   **(1 mark)**

2   Give the relationship between current, potential difference and resistance.

Guided

The current flowing through a .... at constant temperature is

.... to the potential difference across the resistor.   **(2 marks)**

3   (a)   Calculate the potential difference across a resistor which has a resistance of 60 Ω and a current of 0.20 A passing through it.

> You will need to recall the equation: $V = IR$

....

....

....

Potential difference = ... V   **(2 marks)**

    (b)   Calculate the current passing through a 55 Ω resistor with a potential difference of 22 V across it.

....

....

....

Current = ... A   **(2 marks)**

4   (a)   Sketch two lines on the graph to show two ohmic conductors of different resistances. Label these A and B.   **(2 marks)**

Current in A

0   Potential difference in V

    (b)   From your graph, identify which line represents the resistor with the higher resistance.

....   **(1 mark)**

Required practical – Investigating resistance

1 Which of these is the correct method of connecting an ammeter and a voltmeter to determine resistance of a component in a circuit?

Tick **one** box.

Ammeter and voltmeter are both connected in series with the component. ☐

Ammeter is connected in series but voltmeter is connected in parallel across the component. ☐

Ammeter and voltmeter are both connected in parallel across the component. ☐

Voltmeter is connected in series but ammeter is connected in parallel across the component. ☐

(1 mark)

2 Calculate the resistance of a lamp supplied with a current of 1.5 A and a potential difference of 90 V.

> You need to rearrange the equation: $V = IR$

....

....

Resistance of lamp = ... Ω **(2 marks)**

3 Complete the circuit diagram to show how the resistance of a lamp may be obtained using an ammeter and a voltmeter.

Use the components in the box to help you.

⊗   –(V)–   –(A)–

(3 marks)

4 Suggest which components have been tested by looking at the graphs (below) of the data collected.

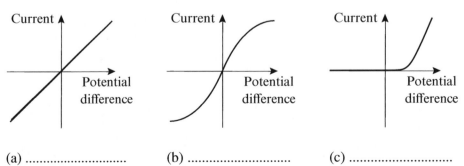

(a) ....   (b) ....   (c) ....   **(3 marks)**

Resistors

1 The *I–V* graphs below show **two** types of component.

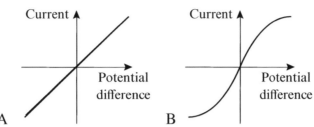

    A   B

(a) Describe what happens to the current through the component shown in **graph A** as the potential difference increases.

....

....

.... **(2 marks)**

(b) Describe what happens to the current through the component shown in **graph B** as the potential difference increases.

....

....

.... **(2 marks)**

2 (a) Complete the *I–V* graphs for a fixed resistor and a filament lamp.

Fixed resistor   Filament lamp

Current ↑   Current ↑

              Potential   Potential
              difference   difference

(2 marks)

(b) Explain why the filament lamp graph has a different shape to the fixed resistor graph (at constant temperature).

> A fixed resistor (at constant temperature) is an ohmic conductor but a filament lamp is not.

....

....

.... **(2 marks)**

3 Describe an experiment to collect data to enable the calculation of the resistance of a wire.

Guided

Data can be collected using an ammeter to measure ....

and a voltmeter to measure ....

A wire should be included and a fixed .... to prevent overheating.

A range of .... measurements should be made so that

resistance can be calculated using the equation .... **(5 marks)**

LDRs and thermistors

1 Identify the variable that will affect the resistance of an LDR.

Tick **one** box.

current ☐

humidity ☐

light ☐

temperature ☐ **(1 mark)**

2 Draw the circuit symbols for the components in the boxes provided.

Light-dependent resistor (LDR)	Thermistor

(2 marks)

3 The sketch graphs below illustrate the relationship between two variables.

Resistance / Light intensity

Resistance / Temperature

(a) Describe how resistance changes with light.

.... **(1 mark)**

(b) Describe how resistance changes with temperature.

.... **(1 mark)**

Guided

4 A car stops at traffic lights. While the car is stationary, the engine is no longer cooled by moving air. A thermistor forms part of a circuit connected to a cooling fan near the engine. Explain the role of the thermistor in the circuit.

The thermistor reacts to a rise in .... in the engine.

Above a certain temperature, it allows .... in the circuit

to flow to a fan, which.. the engine. **(3 marks)**

Practical skills

Required practical – Investigating *I–V* characteristics

1 (a) Complete the diagram below to show how the circuit could be used to investigate the *I–V* characteristics of a range of components.

(2 marks)

(b) Suggest the type of data that should be collected using the circuit above by completing headings for the table below.

These are the dependent and independent variables that you are recording in your experiment.

(i)	(ii)
Data	Data

(2 marks)

(c) Explain why the terminal connections should be reversed to collect additional data.

....

.... **(1 mark)**

(d) Write the labels you would give to the axes on your graph.

y-axis ....

x-axis .... **(1 mark)**

2 (i) Describe what is meant by an ohmic conductor.

....

.... **(1 mark)**

(ii) What happens to the resistance in an ohmic conductor when the potential difference increases?

....

.... **(1 mark)**

3 Identify **one** safety hazard when using resistors in a circuit.

.... **(1 mark)**

Series and parallel circuits

1 (a) Explain the rules for current in series and parallel circuits.

In a series circuit the current flowing through each component is ....

In a parallel circuit, the current is ....

the components. **(2 marks)**

(b) Each lamp in these circuits is identical. Write the
current for each ammeter on the circuit diagrams.

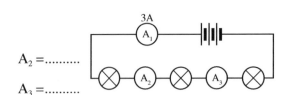

A_2 =..........

A_3 =..........

A_2 = ...

A_3 = ...

A_4 = ... **(2 marks)**

2 (a) Describe the rules for potential difference in series and parallel circuits.

In a series circuit, the total potential difference supplied is ....

....

In a parallel circuit, the potential difference across each component is ....

.... **(2 marks)**

(b) Each lamp in these circuits is identical.
Write the potential difference for each
voltmeter on the circuit diagrams.

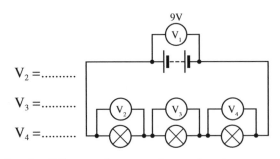

V_2 =..........

V_3 =..........

V_4 =..........

V_2 = ...

V_3 = ...

V_4 = ... **(2 marks)**

3 Describe the difference between the total resistance
of a series circuit and the total resistance of a parallel
circuit, as illustrated below.

> You may find the equation for series
> circuits $R = R_1 + R_2$ helpful in considering
> how current flows.

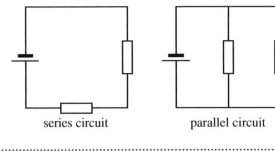

series circuit   parallel circuit

....

....

....

.... **(4 marks)**

ac and dc

1 Circuits can operate using either a direct potential difference and current or an alternating potential difference and current.

(a) Explain what is meant by **direct** potential difference and current.

Direct potential difference is constant and the current flows in the ....

direction.   **(2 marks)**

(b) Explain what is meant by **alternating** potential difference and current.

Alternating potential difference is .... and the current constantly

.... direction.   **(2 marks)**

2 Identify the correct values for potential difference and frequency of the mains supply in the UK.

Tick **one** box.

120 V and 50 Hz   ☐   50 V and 230 Hz   ☐

230 V and 20 Hz   ☐   230 V and 50 Hz   ☐   **(1 mark)**

3 A cell in an electric circuit causes electrons to move along the wires as shown in the diagram.

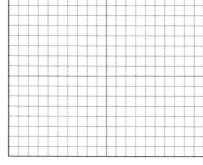

cell

(a) State the type of current supplied by the cell and give a reason for your answer.

Use the diagram to help you.

....

....

.... **(2 marks)**

(b) Complete the graph to show what the trace of the current supplied by the cell would look like on an oscilloscope.

Volts

Time

(1 mark)

Mains electricity

1 (a) Add labels to complete the diagram of a household plug. Use words from the box.

| earth wire | fuse | live wire | neutral |

....
(yellow and green)

....
(brown)

....
(blue)

....

(4 marks)

(b) Explain which wire the fuse is connected to and why.

....

....
(2 marks)

2 The UK domestic mains electricity supply has certain characteristics.

(a) Give the type of current that is delivered through the mains electricity National Grid.

....
(1 mark)

(b) Give the potential difference between the live and neutral wires.

....
(1 mark)

(c) Give the potential difference and purpose of the earth wire.

....

....
(2 marks)

(d) Give the frequency of the domestic electricity supply in the UK.

....
(1 mark)

3 Explain how the fuse in a plug works.

Guided

> A large current can cause a heating effect in the fuse, which is connected to the live wire.

When a large current enters the live wire, this produces ....

.... which .... and

the circuit is then ....
(4 marks)

4 Describe how the earth wire in a plug protects the user if the live wire becomes loose.

....

....

....

....
(3 marks)

Electrical power

1 A hotplate is used to heat up a saucepan of water. The hotplate uses mains voltage of 230 V. The electric current through the hotplate is 5 A. Calculate the power of the hotplate in watts.

Guided

$P = IV = 5 \text{ A} \times$ V

so $P =$ .... W   **(2 marks)**

2 The potential difference across a cell is 6 V. The cell delivers 3 W of power to a filament lamp.

(a) Calculate the current flowing through the lamp.

....

....

....

Current = ... A   **(3 marks)**

(b) A new lamp has a resistance of 240 Ω which draws a current of 0.5 A. Calculate the power rating of the new lamp.

> You need to recall the equation $P = I^2 R$

....

....

....

Power = ... W   **(3 marks)**

3 A coffee maker draws a current of 6 A using a mains voltage of 230 V. The coffee maker is switched on for 15 minutes. Which calculation could be used to determine the power of a coffee maker?

Tick **one** box.

power = (6 × 230 × 15) / 15 (W) ☐   power = 6 × 230 / 15 (W) ☐

power = 6 × 230 / 900 (W) ☐   power = 6 × 230 (W) ☐   **(1 mark)**

4 An 80 V electric drill has a resistance of 8 Ω.

(a) Calculate the current flowing through the drill.

....

....

Current = ... A   **(2 marks)**

(b) Calculate the power of the drill.

....

....

Power = ... W   **(2 marks)**

Electrical energy

1 Identify the quantity that is **not** used to calculate the amount of energy transferred by a device.

Tick **one** box.

current ☐

force ☐

potential difference ☐

time ☐ **(1 mark)**

2 Calculate the amount of energy transferred to a 9 V lamp when a charge of 30 C is supplied.

....

....

Energy transferred = ... J **(2 marks)**

3 A mobile phone has a battery that produces a potential difference of 4 V. When making a call, the phone uses a current of 0.2 A. A student makes a call lasting 30 seconds.

> **Guided**

You need to recall the equations $Q = I\,t$ and $E = Q\,V$

(a) Calculate the charge flow during the phone call.

Charge flow, $Q =$ ....

Charge flow = ... C **(2 marks)**

(b) Calculate the energy transferred by the mobile phone while the call is made. Choose the correct unit from the box.

W	J	V

Energy transferred, $E =$ ....

....

Energy transferred = ... unit................. **(3 marks)**

4 Explain how the energy of a circuit device is related to the following:

(a) Power:

....

.... **(1 mark)**

(b) Potential difference and current:

....

....

....

.... **(2 marks)**

The National Grid

1   The National Grid transmits electricity from power stations at 400 000 volts (400 kV).

(a)   Describe the cause of the heating effect of a current.

....

.... **(2 marks)**

(b)   Explain why this voltage is used to transmit electricity long distances.

> Remember that increasing the voltage decreases the current.

....

....

....

....

.... **(3 marks)**

(c)   Explain how this system can be described as 'efficient'.

....

....

....

.... **(2 marks)**

(d)   Give **one** hazard of transmitting electricity at 400 000 V.

.... **(1 mark)**

2   Describe **two** ways in which energy losses from the National Grid may be reduced.

....

....

....

.... **(2 marks)**

3   Transformers are used at various places in the National Grid. Describe the role of transformers.

Guided

Step-up transformers are used to increase the ....

as it ....

....

Near homes, step-down transformers are used to reduce ....

.... **(4 marks)**

Static electricity

1   Which of the following particles can accumulate to give a static charge?

Tick **one** box.

electrons on conductors   ☐   protons on conductors   ☐

electrons on insulators   ☐   protons on insulators   ☐   **(1 mark)**

2   Describe how a material becomes:

(a) positively charged

....   **(1 mark)**

(b) negatively charged.

....   **(1 mark)**

Guided

3   A student gives a rubber balloon a negative charge by rubbing it on his jumper. He then holds the balloon close to a wall. Explain why the balloon sticks to the wall.

balloon   wall

The balloon has a negative charge.

The student causes a charge on the balloon by ....

from .... to the .... The negative charges on the

balloon repel the ....,

inducing a positive charge on the wall which attracts the negatively charged balloon.

(4 marks)

4   Explain why static charges build up on insulators but not on conductors.

Consider how particles move through the two types of material.

....

....

....

....

....

....

....

....

....   **(5 marks)**

Electric fields

1 Positively charged particles in an electric field will experience a force. Identify **two** positively charged particles.

Tick **two** boxes.

alpha particle ☐

electron ☐

neutron ☐

proton ☐   **(2 marks)**

2 Explain what is meant by the term 'electric field'.

....

....

....

....   **(2 marks)**

3 (a) Draw a diagram to show the electric field of a strong positive point charge.

                                                                                    (3 marks)

(b) An alpha particle is placed in the electric field in part (a). Suggest what happens to the alpha particle and why.

....

....

....

....   **(2 marks)**

4 Describe how the electric field of a charged object changes with distance.

....

....

....

....   **(2 marks)**

Extended response – Electricity

Explain how a circuit can be used to investigate the change in resistance for a thermistor and a light-dependent resistor. Your answer should include a use for each component.

> You will be more successful in extended response questions if you plan your answer before you start writing.
>
> The question asks you to give a detailed explanation of how resistance changes in two types of variable resistor. Think about:
>
> - how resistance in a resistor can be measured and calculated
> - the variable that causes a change in resistance in a thermistor
> - the variable that causes a change in resistance in a light-dependent resistor
> - the consequence to the circuit of a change in resistance in a component
> - uses for thermistors and light-dependent resistors.
>
> You should try to use the information given in the question.

....

....

....

....

....

....

....

....

....

....

....

....

....

....

....

.... **(6 marks)**

Density

1   The diagram below shows the three states of matter for a metal.

(a)   Identify the three states of matter. Write the names in the boxes.   **(1 mark)**

1.	2.	3.

(b)   Describe how mass per unit volume varies with particle arrangement for **each** of the states of matter shown in the diagrams.

....

....

....

....

....   **(3 marks)**

2   Which of these statements correctly describes density?

Tick **one** box.

Density is constant for a substance, whether it is a solid, a liquid or a gas.   ☐

Density is calculated by dividing its mass by its volume.   ☐

Density can be described by weight per unit area.   ☐

Density is calculated by measuring force and volume.   ☐   **(1 mark)**

3   A timber centre collects data on the density of different types of wood.

(a)   Calculate the density of a large block of pine wood with a mass of 1650 kg and a volume of 3 m^3.

> You will need to learn the equation $\rho = m / V$ as it's not on the Physics Equation Sheet.

....

....

Density = ... kg/m^3 **(2 marks)**

(b)   Calculate the density of a block of elm wood with mass 4000 kg and volume 5 m^3.

....

....

Density = ... kg/m^3 **(2 marks)**

Required practical – Investigating density

1 When determining the density of a substance you need to measure the volume of the sample.

(a) Identify which other quantity you need to measure.

.... **(1 mark)**

(b) Give an example of how you could measure this quantity.

.... **(1 mark)**

2 (a) Describe a method that could be used to determine the volume of a regularly shaped solid.

....

....

....

.... **(2 marks)**

(b) Describe a method that could be used to determine the volume of an irregularly shaped solid.

....

....

....

.... **(2 marks)**

3 (a) Describe a method that could be used to find the density of a liquid using a balance.

Place a measuring cylinder on a balance and then zero the scales with ....

....

Add the liquid and .... Record the ....

(in g) from the balance and ....(in cm^3) by reading from the level

in the measuring cylinder. **(3 marks)**

(b) Describe the technique to read the volume of the liquid accurately.

....

....

.... **(2 marks)**

(c) Calculate the density of a liquid with a mass of 121 g and a volume of 205 cm^3.

> You may find this equation useful
>
> $$\text{density} = \frac{\text{mass}}{\text{volume}} \quad \left(\rho = \frac{m}{V} \right)$$

....

....

....

Density = ... g/cm^3 **(2 marks)**

Changes of state

1   Describe the difference between intermolecular forces between particles in a liquid and between particles in a gas.

....

....

....

....   **(2 marks)**

2   Write the type of change that takes place when a substance changes state.

....   **(1 mark)**

3   Water is commonly used to demonstrate changes of state. Complete the sentences to describe the changes of state using words from the box.

| condenses | evaporates | boils | freezes | melts |

When ice is heated beyond 0 °C it .... to become water. The water

is heated and it .... at 100 °C. As heating continues the water

.... and turns to water vapour. As the water vapour is cooled it

.... to become water. As the water cools further it

.... at 0 °C to become ice.   **(3 marks)**

4   Which statement describes the energy change when ice melts and then refreezes?

Tick **one** box.

energy is transferred to surroundings → further energy is transferred to surroundings ☐

energy is transferred to the ice → energy is transferred to surroundings ☐

energy is transferred to surroundings → energy is transferred to the ice ☐

energy is transferred to the ice → energy remains in the system ☐   **(1 mark)**

5   Explain why the temperature stops rising when a liquid is heated to its boiling point and heating continues.

At boiling point, the ....

so the energy applied after boiling point is reached goes into ....

....

The particles .... and become a ....   **(3 marks)**

Internal energy

1 Choose the correct description of internal energy.

Tick **one** box.

the total number of particles in the system ☐

the total sum of the kinetic and potential energies of the particles inside the system ☐

the total number of energies inside the system ☐

the total sum of the kinetic and potential energies of the particles outside the system ☐

(1 mark)

2 A liquid is heated at boiling point before becoming a gas. Describe the change, if any, in the potential and kinetic energies of the particles.

> Remember that latent heat of vaporisation occurs at the boiling point.

liquid   gas

....

....

....

....   **(2 marks)**

3 (a) Describe how internal energy changes when there is a temperature rise in a substance.

....

....

....

....   **(2 marks)**

(b) Describe how internal energy changes when there is no change in temperature.

....

....

....

....   **(2 marks)**

4 Explain the condensation of water vapour in terms of kinetic and potential energies of the particles.

When the water vapour condenses into a liquid there will be no change in the

.... of the water particles so the temperature ....

.... but there will be a .... in the

.... of the water particles as they move

from a gas state to a liquid state.   **(3 marks)**

Specific latent heat

1 Define the term 'specific latent heat'.

.... **(1 mark)**

2 Which of the following remains constant during a change of state?

Tick **one** box.

thermal energy of the mass   ☐

kinetic energy of the particles   ☐

temperature of the mass   ☐

energy supplied to the mass   ☐   **(1 mark)**

3 Calculate the amount of energy needed to melt 25 kg of ice. Take the specific latent heat of fusion of water to be 336 000 J/kg.

....

....

Energy required = ... J   **(2 marks)**

4 Which of the letters A–E on the graph correspond to the following stages during the temperature rise of water over time?

Temperature in °C

(a) Melting ....

(b) Boiling ....

(c) Specific latent heat of fusion ....

(d) Specific latent heat of vaporisation ....   **(4 marks)**

(e) Describe what is happening at stages B and D when there is no rise in temperature.

Consider the bonds between particles.

....

....

.... **(2 marks)**

5 Calculate the energy needed to evaporate 36 kg of water at 100 °C to 36 kg steam at 100 °C.

Take the specific latent heat of vaporisation of water to be 2260 kJ/kg.

....

....

....

Energy needed = ... kJ   **(2 marks)**

Particle motion in gases

1 Describe what is meant by temperature.

> Consider the movement of particles.

....

.... **(1 mark)**

2 The graph below represents the change in pressure with temperature of a gas at constant volume. Describe the relationship shown in the graph between pressure and temperature of the gas.

T in °C

....

.... **(1 mark)**

3 In an experiment, a fixed-volume container of 100 g of helium gas is warmed from −10 °C to 30 °C.

(a) Describe what happens to the velocity of the helium particles as the temperature increases.

As the temperature increases the particles will move ....

because they gain more .... **(2 marks)**

(b) Explain how this affects the pressure on the container walls.

....

....

....

.... **(2 marks)**

(c) Describe what happens to the average kinetic energy of the particles as the temperature increases.

....

.... **(1 mark)**

Pressure in gases

1 Describe the pressure of a gas on a surface in terms of particle movement and force.

When particles of a gas collide with a surface they ....

....

resulting in .... **(3 marks)**

2 When a gas is at constant temperature, what is the relationship between volume and pressure?

Tick **one** box.

Pressure is directly proportional to volume.   ☐

Volume and pressure both decrease.   ☐

Volume is inversely proportional to pressure.   ☐

Pressure and volume both increase.   ☐   **(1 mark)**

3 Use the particle model to explain the following:

(a) Pressure decreases when the volume of a gas, at constant temperature, is increased.

....

....

....

.... **(3 marks)**

(b) Pressure increases when the volume of a gas, at constant temperature, is decreased.

....

....

....

.... **(3 marks)**

4 The pressure in a cylinder of air is increased from atmospheric pressure (100 kPa) to 280 kPa.

The original volume of the cylinder is 230 cm^3.

Calculate the volume of the cylinder when the pressure is 280 kPa.

> You will need to use the correct equation from the Physics Equation Sheet.

....

....

....

....

Volume = ... cm^3 **(3 marks)**

Extended response – Particle model

Substances can undergo a change of state. Explain, using the kinetic particle theory, the changes of state of water. In your answer, include reasons that explain why thermal energy input and output are not always linked to changes in temperature.

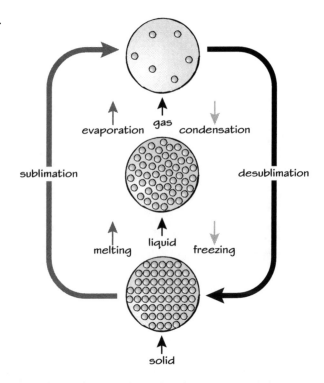

You will be more successful in extended response questions if you plan your answer before you start writing.

The question asks you to give a detailed explanation of how water changes state in terms of particles. Think about:

- the relative kinetic energy of particles in solids, liquids and gases
- why a change of state is described as a reversible change
- how heating the system can result in a change in temperature
- why heating the system does not always result in a change in temperature
- how latent heat is involved in the process.

Include equations to help explain your answer. You should try to use the information given in the question.

....

....

....

....

....

....

....

....

....

.... **(6 marks)**

The structure of the atom

1 Complete the diagram to show the location and charge of:

(a) protons **(1 mark)**

(b) neutrons **(1 mark)**

(c) electrons **(1 mark)**

2 (a) Explain why atoms have no overall charge.

Guided

The number of .... in the nucleus is

.... orbiting the nucleus. **(2 marks)**

(b) Describe what will happen to the overall charge if an atom loses an electron.

.... **(1 mark)**

3 Identify the approximate diameter of an atom and a nucleus from the measurements in the box.

10^{-18} m 10^{-15} m 10^{-10} m 10^{-9} m 10^{-6} m 10^{-2} m

Size of an atom: ....

Size of a nucleus: .... **(2 marks)**

4 The diagram below shows the emission of electromagnetic radiation from an atom.
Describe the process of absorption and emission that would cause this to occur.

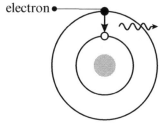

electron

> The diagram shows emission but you will also need to explain the absorption that happens first.

....

....

....

....

....

....

....

.... **(4 marks)**

Atoms, isotopes and ions

1 Describe what is meant by each term.

   (a) Nucleon the name given to particles in the nucleus

   (b) Atomic number ....

   (c) Mass number .... **(3 marks)**

2 Here are some isotopes of lithium.

$$^{6}_{3}\text{Li}, \quad ^{7}_{3}\text{Li}, \quad ^{8}_{3}\text{Li}$$

   Which statement is true?

   Tick **one** box.

   The mass numbers of the atoms are the same.   ☐

   The proton numbers of the atoms are different.   ☐

   The number of neutrons is different.   ☐

   The atoms are of different elements.   ☐   **(1 mark)**

3 Explain why different isotopes of the same
   element will still be neutrally charged.

   > Consider all the particles of the isotopes.

   ....

   ....

   .... **(2 marks)**

4 Some of these symbols show atoms and some
   show ions. Write each symbol in the correct
   part of the table.

   | F^- | Na^+ | B | K^+ | Cu |

Atoms	Ions

   (2 marks)

5 Explain **two** ways in which a neutral atom or molecule can become a positive ion by losing one or
   more electrons.

   ....

   ....

   ....

   ....

   ....

   ....

   .... **(4 marks)**

Models of the atom

1 Bohr developed the nuclear model by describing orbits around the nucleus. Which particle did Bohr propose travelled in this way?

Tick **one** box.

the electron ☐

the proton ☐

the neutron ☐

the positron ☐   **(1 mark)**

2 Compare the plum pudding and nuclear models of the atom.

The plum pudding model showed the atom as ....

.... particle containing ....

....

whereas the nuclear model showed the atom as ....

....

surrounded by .... **(4 marks)**

3 Describe the evidence that led to the nuclear model replacing the plum pudding model.

....

....

....

....

....

.... **(3 marks)**

4 About 20 years after the nuclear model was developed, James Chadwick carried out experiments by firing alpha particles at beryllium atoms. He noticed that a mass was produced close to the size of a proton but was not affected by electrical fields.

(a) Describe the conclusion that Chadwick reached as a result of this observation.

....

....

.... **(2 marks)**

(b) Name the particle that was discovered as a result of Chadwick's experiments.

.... **(1 mark)**

Had a go ☐   Nearly there ☐   Nailed it! ☐

Radioactive decay

1 Complete the following sentences to explain the radioactive process.

(a) Activity is the .... nuclei decay per second. **(2 marks)**

(b) The unit of activity is the .... **(1 mark)**

(c) Count rate is the .... **(2 marks)**

2 Caesium-137 undergoes beta decay. Identify the correct statement.

Tick **one** box.

The positive charge of the nucleus is reduced by 2.   ☐

The number of protons decreases by 1.   ☐

The mass number decreases by 1.   ☐

The number of neutrons decreases by 1.   ☐   **(1 mark)**

3 Identify the correct description of a gamma-ray.

Tick **one** box.

an electron   ☐

electromagnetic radiation   ☐

a neutron   ☐

a proton   ☐   **(1 mark)**

4 In radioactive decay, changes occur in the nucleus. The changes resulting from two different types of radioactive decay are described below. Describe the nature of the radiation, including its name.

> The types of radiation to think about are: α, β, γ and neutron radiation.

(a) The nucleons are reduced by 4.

....

....

....

.... **(2 marks)**

(b) The positive charge of the nucleus increases by 1.

....

....

....

.... **(2 marks)**

Nuclear radiation

1 Select the correct description of an alpha particle.

   Tick **one** box.

   helium nucleus with charge −2   ☐

   helium nucleus with charge +2   ☐

   high-energy neutron   ☐

   ionising electron   ☐   **(1 mark)**

2 Complete the table below.

Type of radiation	Penetrating power
	very low, stopped by 10 cm of air
	low, stopped by thin aluminium
	very high, stopped by very thick lead

                                                                          (2 marks)

3 An atom of carbon-14, with 6 protons and 8 neutrons, undergoes beta decay.

   It becomes an atom of nitrogen, with 7 protons and 7 neutrons.

   (a) Give the change in relative atomic mass.

   ....

   .... **(1 mark)**

   (b) Give another description for a beta particle.

   ....

   .... **(1 mark)**

   (c) Name the relative ionising category of a beta particle.

   ....

   .... **(1 mark)**

4 Describe why alpha particles have the shortest ionising range in air, compared with other types of ionising radiation.

   Compared with other types of ionising radiation, the chance of collision with air

   particles ....

   because ....

   ....

   ....

   .... **(3 marks)**

Uses of nuclear radiation

1 Machinery that produces standard sheets of paper uses radiation to check the thickness.

> Recall the properties of alpha, beta and gamma radiation.

(a) Explain which type of radiation is used.

....

.... **(3 marks)**

(b) A radiation detector measures a sudden drop in the radiation that passes through the paper.

(i) Suggest the most likely cause of this change in radiation detected.

.... **(1 mark)**

(ii) Suggest how the machine would respond to the change.

.... **(1 mark)**

2 Gamma-rays are used to treat cancers. Describe the property of gamma-rays that makes them useful for treating cancers.

.... **(1 mark)**

3 The diagram of the smoke alarm shows that the radioactive isotope americium-241 is used in the system. It is a source of alpha radiation.

> Guided

(a) Explain why it is safe to use smoke detectors in the home.

Alpha particles cannot pass through ....

.... and they are ....

.... **(2 marks)**

(b) Explain why the siren sounds when smoke gets into the smoke alarm.

The smoke particles absorb the alpha

particles ....

....

....

....

....

....

....

smoke entering the alarm

americium-241

siren

air molecules

detector

charged plate

battery

(2 marks)

4 Beta emitters with a short half-life can be used as tracers in the body for medical analysis. Describe the property of beta particles that make them more suitable than alpha particles for monitoring systems in the body.

....

....

.... **(2 marks)**

Nuclear equations

1 Give the symbols used in decay equations to represent the following particles.

   (a) Alpha particle: .... **(1 mark)**

   (b) Beta particle: .... **(1 mark)**

2 Radium-222 undergoes alpha decay. Identify which of the following statements is true.

   Tick **one** box.

   The positive charge of the nucleus is
   reduced by 4.   ☐   The atomic number is increased by 1. ☐

   The mass number is reduced by 4.   ☐   The nucleus gains an extra proton.   ☐ **(1 mark)**

3 Using the data in the table, complete the equations below.

7	9	11	12	14	16	19	20
Li	Be	B	C	N	O	F	Ne
lithium	beryllium	boron	carbon	nitrogen	oxygen	fluorine	neon
3	4	5	6	7	8	9	10
23	24	27	28	29	32	35.5	40
Na	Mg	Al	Si	P	S	Cl	Ar
sodium	magnesium	aluminium	silicon	phosphorus	sulfur	chlorine	argon
11	12	13	14	15	16	17	18

   (a) $^{14}_{6}C \rightarrow ^{14}_{.......}N + ^{0}_{-1}e$ **(1 mark)**

   (b) $^{32}_{......}P \rightarrow ^{32}_{16}S + ^{0}_{-1}e$ **(1 mark)**

4 Identify the type of radiation that would be emitted in
   each decay.   Remember the law of conservation of mass.

   (a) Carbon-10 (6 protons, 4 neutrons) $\rightarrow$ boron-10 (5 protons, 5 neutrons)

        .... **(1 mark)**

   (b) Uranium-238 (92 protons, 146 neutrons) $\rightarrow$ thorium-234 (90 protons, 144 neutrons)

        .... **(1 mark)**

   (c) Helium-5 (2 protons, 3 neutrons) $\rightarrow$ helium-4 (2 protons, 2 neutrons)

        .... **(1 mark)**

5 Complete each equation, naming the
   type of decay shown.   Check that the A and Z numbers obey the conservation laws.

   (a) $^{.......}_{84}Po \rightarrow ^{4}_{2}He + ^{204}_{82}Pb$ Type of decay .... **(2 marks)**

   (b) $^{222}_{......}Rn \rightarrow ^{4}_{2}He + ^{218}_{84}Po$ Type of decay .... **(2 marks)**

   (c) $^{42}_{19}K \rightarrow ^{0}_{-1}e + ^{.......}_{20}Ca$ Type of decay .... **(2 marks)**

   (d) $^{.......}_{4}Be \rightarrow ^{1}_{0}n + ^{8}_{4}Be$ Type of decay .... **(2 marks)**

Half-life

1 Identify the correct term to describe the radioactive decay of an atom.

Tick **one** box.

methodical ☐

regular ☐

random ☐

systematic ☐   **(1 mark)**

2 Define the term 'half-life'.

....

.... **(1 mark)**

3 A sample of thallium-208 contains 16 million atoms. Thallium-208 has a half-life of 3.1 minutes.

(a) Give the number of nuclei that will have decayed in 3.1 minutes.

Number of nuclei = ... **(1 mark)**

(b) Calculate the number of unstable thallium nuclei left after 9.3 minutes.

> Remember that thallium-208 has a half-life of 3.1 minutes, so there are three half-lives in 9.3 minutes.

....

....

Number of thallium nuclei after 9.3 min = ... **(2 marks)**

4 A student measured the activity of a radioactive sample for 30 minutes. She plotted the graph of activity against time shown on the right.

Guided

Radioactive decay

Count rate in becquerels

Use the graph to work out the half-life of the sample.

Starting activity = ... Bq at .... minutes.

Half this activity = ... Bq, at .... minutes,

so the half-life is .... minutes.   **(3 marks)**

Contamination and irradiation

1 Identify the correct term for when a person or object is exposed to nuclear radiation.

Tick **one** box.

decontamination ☐   irradiation ☐

fusion ☐   radioactive decay ☐   **(1 mark)**

2 Define the following terms about exposure to radiation.

(a) External contamination

....

.... **(1 mark)**

(b) Internal contamination

....

.... **(1 mark)**

(c) Irradiation

....

.... **(1 mark)**

3 Give an example of how a person may be subjected to:

(a) external contamination

.... **(1 mark)**

(b) internal contamination

.... **(1 mark)**

4 Explain why alpha particles are more dangerous from a source of internal contamination than external contamination.

> Alpha particles travel only a very short distance before colliding with another particle, losing their energy. This can have serious consequences near to the body.

....

....

....

....

....

....

.... **(4 marks)**

Hazards of radiation

1 Identify the most ionising radiation.

Tick **one** box.

alpha particles ☐   gamma-rays ☐

beta particles ☐   X-rays ☐   **(1 mark)**

2 Suggest **three** precautions that may be taken by people who may come into contact with ionising radiation to reduce the risk of cell damage.

1. ....

2. ....

3. .... **(3 marks)**

3 Explain why alpha particles are more dangerous inside the body than gamma-rays.

A source of alpha particles with high activity inside the body ....

.... because they ....

before transferring all of their ionising energy.

Gamma-rays can ....

without .... **(4 marks)**

4 When radioactive sources are handled, tongs are often used. Explain why those handling radioactive sources would use tongs.

radioactive source

....

....

....

.... **(2 marks)**

5 X-rays can also be ionising to body cells. Suggest why it is considered safe for the patient to be exposed to the X-rays whereas the medical workers have to leave the room.

....

....

....

....

.... **(3 marks)**

Think about what could happen to those working regularly with radioactive sources if they did not leave the room when using these.

Background radiation

1 The pie chart shows the sources of background radiation in the UK.

> Radioactive isotopes are often produced when larger radioactive isotopes decay.

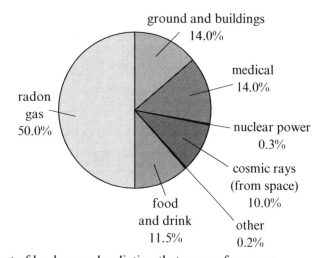

ground and buildings 14.0%
medical 14.0%
nuclear power 0.3%
cosmic rays (from space) 10.0%
other 0.2%
food and drink 11.5%
radon gas 50.0%

Determine approximately the amount of background radiation that comes from non-natural sources.

....

.... **(1 mark)**

Guided

2 Give **two** reasons why radon levels can vary across the UK.

1. Levels can vary because of ....

   that occur naturally in the environment.

2. They can also vary due to the use of different rocks such as ....

   .... in buildings.   **(2 marks)**

3 Complete the table by giving examples of natural and man-made sources of background radiation.

Sources of background radiation	
Natural	**Man-made**

> Use the pie chart in question 1 to help you.

(3 marks)

4 Two scientists in different parts of the country measure the background radiation count three times. Their results are shown in the table below.

Test number	1	2	3	Average
South East activity (Bq)	0.30	0.24	0.27	
South West activity (Bq)	0.31	0.28	0.32	

(a) Calculate the average activity for each sample and write it in the table.

.... **(1 mark)**

(b) Suggest which area has the highest average level of background radiation.

.... **(1 mark)**

Medical uses

1 Gamma radiation can be used in medical centres to destroy unwanted tissue. Which of these statements explains why gamma radiation is used?

Tick **one** box.

Gamma radiation is more easily absorbed by cells than alpha or beta radiation. ☐

Gamma radiation penetrates deeper from outside the body than alpha or beta radiation. ☐

Gamma radiation is applied using a wide beam of radiation. ☐

Radioactive isotopes used have a very long half-life. ☐   **(1 mark)**

2 Describe how a cancer tumour can be treated using gamma-rays.

> Several beams of gamma-rays are aimed at the same point in the body.

....

....

....

....

....

.... **(3 marks)**

3 Describe what is meant by a medical tracer, including how it is used.

A medical tracer is a ....

....

It is injected into the patient and is then ....

....

A special camera detects the ....

....

The detected waves are used to build up an image of ....

.... **(4 marks)**

4 The radioactive isotope used in medicine to produce gamma radiation must be carefully selected to have the appropriate half-life. Suggest **two** reasons why half-life is important in medicine.

....

....

....

.... **(2 marks)**

Nuclear fission

1   Label the particles shown in the diagram of nuclear fission. Use the words in the box below.

| neutrons | daughter nuclei | uranium-235 |

....

....

energy release

....

(3 marks)

2   (a)   Define the term 'nuclear fission'.

....

.... **(2 marks)**

(b)   Spontaneous fission is rare. Explain what must usually happen for fission to occur.

....

.... **(2 marks)**

3   (a)   Describe what is meant by the term 'chain reaction'.

....

....

....

.... **(3 marks)**

(b)   Describe the measures taken to control a chain reaction in a nuclear reactor.

Control measures are used to stop the process going out of control.

....

....

.... **(2 marks)**

(c)   Draw a diagram to illustrate a chain reaction.

(4 marks)

(d)   Identify where controlled chain reactions are used.

.... **(1 mark)**

Nuclear fusion

1 Which statement is a correct example of fusion?

Tick **one** box.

helium nuclei → hydrogen nuclei   ☐

hydrogen nuclei → helium nuclei   ☐

uranium nuclei → thorium nuclei   ☐

plutonium → uranium nuclei   ☐   **(1 mark)**

2 In 1989 Martin Fleischmann and Stanley Pons announced that they had performed nuclear fusion in a process that newspaper reporters called 'cold fusion'. Since then, however, other scientists have been unable to repeat the experiment.

Explain why it has been difficult for Fleischmann and Pons to prove that their experiments were successful.

> Recall the scientific method and how it is applied.

....

....

....

.... **(2 marks)**

3 (a) Identify where fusion occurs naturally in the Solar System.

.... **(1 mark)**

(b) Identify a product of fusion experienced on Earth.

.... **(1 mark)**

(c) Identify other places where fusion occurs naturally.

.... **(1 mark)**

4 (a) Describe why the process of nuclear fusion is so difficult to achieve.

....

....

.... **(2 marks)**

(b) Describe what would be needed to overcome the difficulties of the nuclear fusion process.

....

....

....

.... **(3 marks)**

Extended response – Radioactivity

Ionising radiation will travel through some materials but will be stopped by others. The diagram shows three different materials and how alpha, beta or gamma radiation may be absorbed by each one.

Use the diagram to help you describe the structure and properties of these three types of radiation. In your answer, name the materials that could be shown in the diagram, and give other examples of how these types of radioactivity may be absorbed.

helium nucleus
= α emission

electron
= β emission

electromagnetic radiation
= γ emission

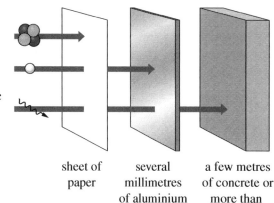

sheet of paper   several millimetres of aluminium   a few metres of concrete or more than 10 cm of lead

You will be more successful in extended response questions if you plan your answer before you start writing.

The question asks you to give a detailed explanation of the penetrative characteristics of ionising radiation and examples of materials that may stop the radiation. Think about:

- the relative ionising abilities of alpha, beta and gamma radiation
- how energy is transferred when radiation encounters a particle
- the effect that particle collisions have on how radiation passes through a material
- examples of materials that absorb different types of radiation.

You should try to use the information given in the diagram.

....

....

....

....

....

....

....

....

....

....

....

....

.... **(6 marks)**

Scalars and vectors

1 (a) Complete the table using the examples of scalars and vectors from the box below.

| acceleration | displacement | speed | energy | temperature |
| mass | force | velocity | momentum | distance |

Scalars	Vectors

(2 marks)

(b) Give one example of a scalar from the table, and explain why it is a scalar.

.... is a scalar because it has a size / magnitude but no

.... **(3 marks)**

2 (a) Which of the following is **not** a scalar?

Tick **one** box.

energy ☐   temperature ☐   mass ☐   weight ☐   **(1 mark)**

(b) Give a reason for your answer to (a).

.... **(1 mark)**

3 Two students set off jogging in opposite directions. The first student starts to jog to the east at a velocity of 2 m/s. The second student jogs to the west at a velocity of −2 m/s.

(a) (i) Explain why velocity is used in this example rather than speed.

.... **(1 mark)**

(ii) Explain why the velocity for the student jogging to the west is given a negative value.

.... **(1 mark)**

(b) Explain the importance of the length of the diagram arrows. Describe how you would draw the arrow if student 2 sped up to 3 m/s.

....

....

....

.... **(2 marks)**

Interacting forces

1 Name the **three** types of fields that cause objects to interact with each other without making contact.

1. ....   2. ....   3. ....   **(3 marks)**

2 Which of the following statements correctly describes the similarities between magnetic and electrostatic fields?

Tick **one** box.

Like poles and charges repel.   ☐

Like poles and charges attract.   ☐

Opposite poles and charges have a null point.   ☐

Opposite poles and charges repel.   ☐   **(1 mark)**

3 Describe the differences and similarities between weight and normal contact force.

Weight and normal contact forces are both vectors because ....

....

Weight is measured .... whereas normal contact force is

measured ....   **(3 marks)**

4 A student pulls a wheeled suitcase, as shown in the diagram, at constant velocity.

(a) Name the contact forces that are balanced for the horizontal plane.

....   **(1 mark)**

(b) Name the balanced contact forces in the vertical direction.

....   **(1 mark)**

5 A skydiver jumps from an aeroplane. Explain which forces influence the descent of the skydiver and how the net result of the forces controls how the skydiver descends, at each stage.

> Make sure your answer includes the terms air resistance, terminal velocity and speed.

....

....

....

....

....

....   **(4 marks)**

Gravity, weight and mass

1   The lunar roving vehicle (LRV) has a mass of 210 kg on Earth.

Guided   (a) Give the mass of the LRV on the Moon and a reason for your answer.

The mass of the LRV on the Moon is .... kg because...........................

.... **(2 marks)**

(b) Draw an arrow on the LRV to show where the centre of mass would act and explain
what is meant by centre of mass (in the space below).

.... **(2 marks)**

2   Calculate the total weight of a backpack of mass 1 kg, containing books with a mass of
2 kg and trainers with a mass of 1.5 kg. Take gravitational field strength (*g*) to be 10 N/kg.

> You will find the equation $W = m\,g$ useful.

....

....

....

....

....

Weight = ... N **(2 marks)**

3   A student is about to fly to Europe. The total baggage allowance is 20 kg. The student
has scales that weigh only in newtons. Determine the items that she can take on holiday,
as well as her clothes, to get as close to 20 kg as possible. Show your calculations. Take
gravitational field strength to be 10 N/kg.

> Remember to convert the weights shown to masses before you add them up.

laptop	camera bag	walking boots	jacket	clothes
45 N	55 N	25 N	35 N	105 N

....

....

....

....

Total baggage = ... kg **(3 marks)**

Resultant forces

1   Define the term 'resultant force'.

....

.... **(1 mark)**

2   Below are diagrams of pairs of forces.

A ⬆ ⬆ 5 N   4.5 N   B ⬆ ⬇ 6 N   4 N   C ⇨ ⇦ 7 N   2.5 N   D ⇦ ⇦ 5.5 N   7.25 N

resultant = ... N   resultant = ... N   resultant = ... N   resultant = ... N

direction ....   direction ....   direction ....   direction ....

(a) Calculate the value of the resultant force for each pair.   **(4 marks)**

(b) Draw an arrow to show the direction of each resultant force.   **(4 marks)**

3   The diagram shows a pair of forces.

What is the magnitude of the resultant force?

Tick **one** box.

3 N   ☐

4 N   ☐

20 N ☐

7 N   ☐

⬆ 8 N

⬇ 12 N   **(1 mark)**

4   A speed skater is standing on the ice waiting for the start of a race. The race begins and the skater starts to push against the ice, producing a forward thrust on the skates of 30 N. There is resistance from the air of 10 N and friction on the blades of 1 N.

(a) Calculate the resultant force.

> Add up all the forces in a straight line. Think about the direction of each force.

Resultant force = positive direction – negative direction = ...

....

Force = ... N **(2 marks)**

(b) During the race, the resistive forces become equal to the forward thrust. Explain what happens to the velocity of the skater.

....

....

....

.... **(2 marks)**

Work and energy

1 Which of these is the energy equivalent to the work done when a force is moved through a vertical distance?

Tick **one** box.

gravitational potential energy ☐   latent heat ☐

kinetic energy ☐   specific heat capacity ☐   **(1 mark)**

2 (a) Explain why friction may result in wasted energy when moving an object through a distance.

> **Guided**

Work done against friction will lead to ....

....

this energy is then dissipated to .... **(2 marks)**

(b) Explain the consequence of friction in terms of work needed to be done in moving an object.

The greater the amount of friction ....

....

to move the body through .... **(2 marks)**

3 A suitcase is pulled along a walkway with a force of 80 N. The suitcase is pulled a distance of 60 m. Calculate the work done on the suitcase.

> You should be able to recall the equation $W = F\,s$; it won't be provided on the Physics Equation Sheet.

....

....

Work done = ... J   **(2 marks)**

4 A student designs a pulley system to lift a mass of 8 kg.

The energy transferred by the force of the pulley is 320 J.

(a) Calculate the height to which the pulley system lifts the mass. Take g to be 10 N/kg.

> You should be able to recall the equation $E_p = m\,g\,h$; it won't be provided on the Physics Equation Sheet.

....

....

Height = ... m   **(2 marks)**

(b) Use your answer from (a) to calculate the force exerted by the pulley system.

....

....

Force = ... N   **(3 marks)**

Forces and elasticity

1   Identify the force that would act opposite to the forward motion of a bicycle.

Tick **one** box.

upthrust ☐

reaction force ☐

friction ☐

tension ☐   **(1 mark)**

2   Give an example where each of the following may occur:

(a) tension

.... **(1 mark)**

(b) compression

.... **(1 mark)**

(c) elastic distortion

.... **(1 mark)**

(d) inelastic distortion

.... **(1 mark)**

3   A student investigates loading two aluminium beams, each with an elastic limit at 50 N. Beam 1 is tested to 45 N. Beam 2 is tested to 60 N.

Guided

Predict what you would expect the beams to look like after loading.

Explain your answer.

After testing, Beam 1 would return to the same size and shape as ....

.... and would be intact.

Beam 2 would ....

but would (probably) .... **(4 marks)**

Force and extension

1 Describe the difference between elastic deformation and inelastic deformation caused by stretching forces.

....

....

....

....

....

....

....

.... **(4 marks)**

2 A force is added to a spring. The extension of the spring is 0.04 m and the spring constant is 500 N/m. Calculate the force.

Tick **one** box.

0.02 N ☐   2 N ☐

0.2 N ☐   20 N ☐   **(1 mark)**

3 A spring is stretched from 0.03 m to 0.07 m, within its elastic limit. Calculate the force needed to stretch the spring. Select the correct unit from the box below. Take the spring constant to be 80 N/m.

> Guided

kg	m	N

Extension = 0.07 m – .... m = ... m

Force = ... × extension = ... × ....

Force = ... unit .... **(3 marks)**

4 (a) Calculate the spring constant (k) of a spring that is stretched 15 cm when a force of 30 N is applied.

....

....

k = ... N/m **(3 marks)**

(b) Calculate the energy transferred to the spring in (a).

> You need to select the equation:
>
> energy = ½ × spring constant × extension²
>
> from the Physics Equation Sheet.

....

....

Energy transferred = ... J **(2 marks)**

Required practical – Force and extension

1 (a) Describe how to set up an experiment to investigate the elastic potential energy stored in a spring using a spring, a ruler, masses or weights, a clamp and a stand.

> Include a step to make sure the spring is not damaged during the experiment.

....

....

....

....

....

.... **(4 marks)**

(b) Explain why it is important to check that the spring is not damaged during the experiment.

....

....

.... **(2 marks)**

(c) Describe how the data collected must be processed before a graph can be plotted. Assume masses are used and measurements made in mm.

Guided

Masses must be converted to ....

The extension of the spring must be ....

....

Extension measurements should be .... **(3 marks)**

(d) Describe how a graph plotted from this experiment can be used to calculate:

(i) the elastic potential energy stored in the spring

.... **(1 mark)**

(ii) the spring constant *k*.

.... **(1 mark)**

(e) Name the point on the graph that represents where the spring begins to permanently change shape.

.... **(1 mark)**

(f) Write the equation to calculate the energy stored by the spring.

.... **(1 mark)**

2 Explain the difference between the length of a spring and the extension of a spring.

....

.... **(1 mark)**

Moments

1 Identify which of the following describes a moment.

Tick **one** box.

a force acting in a clockwise-only direction ☐

a perpendicular force acting at a distance from a pivot ☐

a force acting perpendicular to a surface ☐

a force that causes bending to occur ☐   **(1 mark)**

2 Describe the principle of moments for balanced objects.

> **Guided**

When an object is balanced the clockwise moment is equal to ....

.... **(2 marks)**

3 A screwdriver is used to remove the lid from a tin of paint. Calculate the moment of the screwdriver when a force of 25 N is applied at 0.28 m from the lip of the paint lid. Select the unit from the box below.

N	N m	m

....

....

Moment = ... unit.............   **(3 marks)**

4 Two children, A and B, play on a seesaw. A has a mass of 25 kg and sits 1.2 m from the pivot.

B has a mass of 30 kg and sits 0.8 m from the pivot on the opposite side to A. Take g to be 10 N/kg.

(a) Determine whether the moments that the children exert on the seesaw are in equilibrium. Write down any equation that you use.

> Remember to calculate all the quantities first so that you can use them in the correct equation. You should write down all your calculations. You need to recall the equation $M = F d$ because it's not on the Physics Equation Sheet.

....

....

....

.... **(3 marks)**

(b) Calculate the distance from the pivot B must sit to make the moments balance.

> The new balancing moment for B must equal the moment for A in part (a).

....

....

Distance = ... m   **(2 marks)**

Levers and gears

1 Identify which of the following statements correctly describes levers and gears.

Tick **one** box.

Levers and gears transmit the torsional effect of forces.   ☐

Levers and gears transmit the rotational effects of forces.   ☐

Levers and gears transmit the tensile effect of forces.   ☐

Levers and gears transmit the compressional effect of forces.   ☐   **(1 mark)**

2 (a) Complete the diagrams of typical levers below by adding the following labels.

   (i)   input force   **(1 mark)**

   (ii) output force   **(1 mark)**

   (iii) pivot   **(1 mark)**

   (b) Explain the terms 'input force' and 'output force'.

   ....

   ....

   ....

   ....   **(2 marks)**

3 Explain the difference between a high gear and a low gear.

For a high gear, the driver gear has a greater diameter than the driven gear, and

the output is.. for a given input force.

For a low gear, the driver gear has ....

to the .... and the ....

.... **(4 marks)**

59

Pressure

1 Pressure in fluids causes a force. Choose the correct description of how this force acts on a surface.

Tick **one** box.

Pressure in fluids causes a force to act parallel to a surface.   ☐

Pressure in fluids causes a force to act at right angles to the surface.   ☐

Pressure in fluids causes a force to act at an angle of 180° to the surface.   ☐

Pressure in fluids causes a force to act at an angle of 45° to the surface.   ☐   **(1 mark)**

2 Calculate the pressure exerted by a rectangular block with an area of 0.0625 m² with a force of 25 N.

> You should remember $P = F / A$ because it won't be given on the Physics Equation Sheet.

....

....

Pressure = ... Pa   **(2 marks)**

3 A square wooden box exerts a pressure of 2000 Pa over an area of 0.25 m².
Calculate the weight of the box.

Guided

> Remember that weight is a type of force.

The weight of the box is found by ....

....

Weight = ... N   **(2 marks)**

4 (a) Explain what is meant by atmospheric pressure.

Guided

Atmospheric pressure describes a column of air reaching from ....

....,

and covering ....

containing a mass of air equal to...   **(3 marks)**

(b) Calculate the total force on a football pitch due to atmospheric pressure. The area of the football pitch is 5000 m². Take atmospheric pressure to be 100 000 Pa.

> Remember to rearrange the equation for pressure first.

$p = \frac{F}{A}$ so F...

Force = ... N   **(2 marks)**

Distance and displacement

1 The diagram shows different points on a field.

Which of these is the correct displacement from A when a footballer warms up by running from points A to B, B to D and D to C?

Tick **one** box.

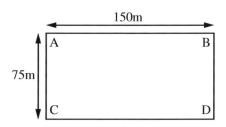

A to B to D to C = 375 m   ☐   A to C = 75 m   ☐

AB × AC = 11 250 m   ☐   AB + AC = 225 m   ☐   **(1 mark)**

2 Explain why distance is described as a scalar quantity but displacement is described as a vector quantity.

Distance does not involve .... and so is a scalar quantity.

Displacement involves both ....

.... so it is a vector quantity. **(2 marks)**

3 Two girls step into a pod on the Ferris wheel when it reaches the bottom and stops. The diameter of the Ferris wheel is 15 m. The wheel completes three cycles before the girls step off again at the bottom.

  (a) Calculate the distance that the girls have travelled at the end of the ride.

> Use 2 π r to calculate the circumference of a circle.

....

....

....

.... **(3 marks)**

  (b) Explain the final displacement of the girls at the end of the ride.

....

....

....

.... **(2 marks)**

Speed and velocity

1 A bus travels from the bus station to the next town 10 kilometres away, passing through three villages on the way, picking up passengers at each village. The whole trip takes 40 minutes. Calculate the average speed of the bus.

> You will need to recall the equation
> average speed = distance / time
> as it's not on the Physics Equation Sheet.

....

....

Average speed = ... m/s   **(2 marks)**

2 (a) The speed of runners often varies during a cross-country race. Suggest **three** factors that could affect the speed of the runners.

....

.... **(3 marks)**

(b) Give typical speeds for the following:

(i) a person walking .... **(1 mark)**

(ii) a person running .... **(1 mark)**

(iii) a person cycling .... **(1 mark)**

3 A satellite orbits the Earth with a constant speed of 3100 m/s.

Explain how the speed of the satellite can be constant while the velocity is constantly changing.

> Guided

The speed of the satellite is constant because the ....,

.... but the velocity changes constantly because the

.... **(2 marks)**

4 A rowing team launches a boat from the boathouse and rows up the river in a north-west direction for 15 minutes at an average velocity of 4 m/s.

> You will need to recall the equation $s = v\,t$
> because it's not on the Physics Equation Sheet.

(a) Calculate the distance covered by the rowing team.

....

....

Distance = ... m   **(2 marks)**

(b) Explain why the term 'velocity' is used instead of 'speed' to describe the journey.

....

....

.... **(2 marks)**

(c) Describe how the displacement of the team changes as they make their way from the boathouse to finishing the journey by boat and returning to the boathouse by bus.

> Guided

At the finish of the journey by boat the displacement of the team from the boathouse

is .... m.

As they return to the boathouse by bus, the displacement .... until they arrive

back at the boathouse where the final displacement is .... m.   **(3 marks)**

Distance–time graphs

1 The distance–time graph shows a runner's journey from home to the park.

   (a) Give the letter on the graph that corresponds to the part of the runner's journey where he:

       (i)   stops ....

       (ii) runs fastest. .... **(2 marks)**

Distance in m

   (b) Calculate the speed of
        the runner between
        70 s and 110 s.

   > Your answer should show ALL
   > your working.

Time in s

   ....

   ....

   ....

   .... m/s **(3 marks)**

   (c) Explain whether the runner was running or walking for the last part of the journey.

   ....

   ....

   ....

   .... **(2 marks)**

   (d) Calculate the runner's speed in part A of his journey.

   In part A, he travels .... m in .... s.

   speed = $\dfrac{distance}{.............................}$

                                        Speed = ... m/s **(3 marks)**

   (e) When the runner arrives at the park his displacement from home is less than the distance he has
        travelled. Explain this difference.

   ....

   ....

   ....

   .... **(2 marks)**

Velocity–time graphs

1 A cyclist takes 5 seconds to accelerate from rest to 4 m/s. The cyclist moves in a straight line.

Calculate the cyclist's acceleration.

Select the unit from the box below.

> You will need to recall and apply the equation $a = \Delta v / t$ as it's not on the Physics Equation Sheet.

s	m/s	m/s²

....

....

....

Acceleration = ... unit.............. **(3 marks)**

2 The velocity–time graph below shows how the velocity of a car changes with time.

(a) This graph can be used to analyse the car's journey. Identify the statement that describes the information shown by the gradient of the graph.

Tick **one** box.

The velocity of the car is increasing steadily. ☐

The velocity of the car is constant. ☐

The car is decelerating. ☐

The acceleration of the car is changing. ☐   **(1 mark)**

(b) Draw on the graph to show how velocity and time taken can be used to calculate acceleration. **(1 mark)**

(c) Calculate the acceleration of the car.

> Guided

Change in velocity = ... m/s. Time taken for the change = ... s.

Acceleration = $\dfrac{\text{change in velocity}}{\text{time taken}}$ = ... m/s²

Acceleration = ... m/s² **(2 marks)**

Equations of motion

1   Choose the typical acceleration of a car accelerating away from traffic lights.

Tick **one** box.

0.04 m/s^2 ☐

0.4 m/s^2 ☐

4 m/s^2 ☐

40 m/s^2 ☐   **(1 mark)**

2   (a)   A racing car takes 8 seconds to speed up from 15 m/s to 25 m/s. Calculate its acceleration.

> You will need to recall $a = \Delta v / t$ because it is not given on the Physics Equation Sheet.

....

....

....

Acceleration = ... m/s^2 **(3 marks)**

(b)   The same racing car now accelerates at the same rate for 12 seconds, from 25 m/s to a higher velocity. It travels 300 m during this time.
Calculate its final velocity.

> You need to select, and rearrange, the equation $v^2 - u^2 = 2as$ from the Physics Equation Sheet.

....

....

....

....

Velocity = ... m/s   **(3 marks)**

(c)   The same racing car now slows down to 5 m/s from the velocity calculated in (b) at a rate of −2 m/s^2.
Calculate how far the car travels when decelerating to this new final velocity.

....

....

....

Distance = ... m   **(3 marks)**

Terminal velocity

1   An object that falls near to the Earth's surface is said to be in free fall. Identify the influence that causes the object to accelerate.

Tick **one** box.

air resistance ☐   gravity ☐

terminal velocity ☐   friction ☐   **(1 mark)**

2   An experienced skydiver undergoes freefall before opening her parachute, during which she reaches a speed of around 55 m/s.

(a) Explain why the skydiver accelerates to this speed.

> Guided

The force of gravity pulls the skydiver downwards. ....

.... **(2 marks)**

(b) Explain why the skydiver stops accelerating at around this speed even before the parachute is opened. Refer to 'resultant force' in your answer.

> The resultant force is 0 N when two forces are in balance.

The skydiver stops accelerating because the air resistance ....

.... **(2 marks)**

(c) Give the name for the speed reached by the skydiver before she opens her parachute.

.... **(1 mark)**

(d) Explain what happens to the speed of the skydiver once the parachute is opened.

> Guided

The larger surface area increases air resistance ....

....

.... **(3 marks)**

3   A student investigates terminal velocity by dropping a ball-bearing in a very long column of viscous liquid.

Suggest how the student could measure the terminal velocity of the ball-bearing.

> The student will need to recall and rearrange the equation $s = v\,t$

....

....

....

....

....

....

.... **(4 marks)**

Newton's first law

1 (a) An aeroplane is waiting to take off and is stationary. Use Newton's first law to explain why it remains stationary.

    ....

    ....

    .... **(2 marks)**

   (b) The aeroplane takes off and then flies at constant speed and constant height. Use Newton's first law to explain why it remains flying at a constant speed and height.

    ....

    ....

    .... **(2 marks)**

2 A speed skater is standing on the ice waiting for the start of a race.

   (a) The race begins and the skater pushes against the ice producing a forward-driving force on the skates of 30 N. There is resistance from the air of 5 N and friction on the blades of 1 N. Calculate the resultant force forward.

    > Consider all the forces in a straight line. Forces that act opposite to the driving force should have a negative sign.

    ....

    ....

    Force = ... N **(2 marks)**

   (b) During the race, the resistive forces become equal to the forward driving force. Explain what happens to the velocity of the skater.

    ....

    ....

    .... **(2 marks)**

3 A space probe falls towards the Moon. In the Moon's gravitational field, the probe has a weight of 1700 N. After a period of free fall, the probe thrusters are fired briefly, providing an upward driving force of 1900 N.

   (a) Calculate the resultant force on the space probe when the thrusters are firing. Assume that the positive direction is downwards.

    ....

    ....

    Resultant force = ... N **(2 marks)**

   (b) Describe the changes in the probe's velocity when the thrusters are firing.

    ....

    ....

    .... **(2 marks)**

Newton's second law

1 In an experiment a student pulls a force meter attached to a trolley along a bench. The trolley has frictionless wheels. The force meter gives a reading of 5 N.

trolley   force meter

Guided

(a) Describe what happens to the trolley.

The trolley will ....

in the direction .... **(2 marks)**

(b) The student stacks some masses on the trolley and again pulls it with a force of 5 N.

Explain why the trolley takes longer to travel the length of the bench.

The acceleration is .... because .... **(2 marks)**

2 A minibus with passengers has a mass of 3000 kg and slows down with an average acceleration of −3 m/s².

(a) Calculate the average force acting on the minibus.

....

....

Force = ... N **(2 marks)**

(b) Give the direction in which the force acts.

.... **(1 mark)**

3 A Formula One racing car has a mass of 640 kg. A resultant force of 10 500 N acts on the car.

(a) Calculate the acceleration of the racing car. Choose the unit from the box below.

m/s²	m/s	N

Remember that Newton's second law refers to $F = m\,a$

....

....

Acceleration = ... unit .... **(3 marks)**

(b) Explain what will happen to the acceleration of the car as its fuel tank empties, assuming that the resultant force remains constant and the tank never fully empties.

....

....

....

.... **(2 marks)**

Practical skills

Required practical – Force, mass and acceleration

A ramp, a trolley, masses and electronic light gates can be used to investigate the relationship between force, mass and acceleration.

1   Explain **one** advantage of using electronic measuring equipment to determine acceleration compared to using a ruler and stopwatch.

> Think about human reaction times compared to using electronic equipment.

....

....

.... **(2 marks)**

2   Describe the relationship between acceleration and mass.

....   **(1 mark)**

3   Explain why it is necessary to use two light gates when measuring acceleration in this experiment.

Acceleration is calculated by the change in speed / time taken, so ....

....

.... **(2 marks)**

4   (a)   Describe the conclusion that can be drawn from this experiment.

For a constant slope...

....

.... **(2 marks)**

    (b)   Identify which of Newton's laws can be referred to in verifying the results of this experiment.

> The quantities of force, mass and acceleration are linked in this equation.

.... **(1 mark)**

5   Suggest **one** hazard associated with this experiment and **two** safety precautions that could be taken to minimise the risk of harm to the scientist.

> Consider the potential dangers of using accelerated masses or electrical equipment.

....

....

....

....

.... **(3 marks)**

Newton's third law

1   Which of these statements summarises Newton's third law?

Tick **one** box.

For every action there is a constant reaction.   ☐

The action and reaction forces are different due to friction.   ☐

Reaction forces may be stationary or at constant speed.   ☐

For every action there is an equal and opposite reaction.   ☐   **(1 mark)**

2   Before lift-off, a massive rocket sits on the launch pad.
Use Newton's third law to explain why the rocket
does not fall through the launch pad, in spite of
its weight.

....

....

....

....

(2 marks)

3   The image shows a penguin standing on ice. Explain how action–
reaction force pairs act on the penguin and why they are in
equilibrium.

....

....

....

....

(2 marks)

4   Buttresses are used in architecture to strengthen walls by achieving an equilibrium of
forces as they push against heavy stone walls that tend to push outwards under their own
weight. Using Newton's third law, explain why buttresses are used.

Newton's third law says that the forces must be equal in ....

and .... in direction to be in equilibrium. The force exerted by

the buttresses on the .... is equal and opposite to the

force exerted on the ....by the building, resulting in no

movement occurring.   **(4 marks)**

Stopping distance

1 (a) Give the word equation used to calculate overall stopping distance.

.... **(1 mark)**

(b) Complete the table below to summarise the factors that affect overall stopping distance.

> Separate the factors that may affect the reaction time of a driver from those that affect the vehicle.

Factors increasing overall stopping distance	
Thinking distance will increase if	**Braking distance will increase if**
	the car's speed increases
the driver is distracted	

(2 marks)

2 (a) Describe what happens when a force is applied to the brakes of a vehicle.

....

....

....

....

....

.... **(3 marks)**

(b) Explain what happens to the temperature of the brakes.

....

....

....

.... **(2 marks)**

3 Recent proposals have been made to increase the national speed limit in certain cases. Suggest how these proposals might increase the risk of damage to vehicles and their passengers.

> Remember that kinetic energy is proportional to v^2.

....

....

....

....

....

.... **(3 marks)**

Reaction time

1 The chart below includes typical thinking distances covered by vehicles at different speeds.

20 mph (32 km/h)	6 m → 6 m →	= **12 m (40 ft)** or 3 car lengths
30 mph (48 km/h)	9 m → 14 m →	= **23 m (75 ft)** or 6 car lengths
40 mph (64 km/h)	12 m → 24 m →	= **36 m (118 ft)** or 9 car lengths
50 mph (80 km/h)	15 m → 38 m →	= **53 m (175 ft)** or 13 car lengths
60 mph (96 km/h)	18 m → 55 m →	= **73 m (240 ft)** or 18 car lengths
70 mph (112 km/h)	21 m → 75 m →	= **96 m (315 ft)** or 24 car lengths

Average car length = 4 metres (13ft)

The distances shown are a general guide. The distance will depend on your attention (thinking distance), the road surface, the weather conditions and the condition of your vehicle at the time.

■ Thinking distance
▨ Braking distance

Identify the expected effect on overall stopping distance, if the driver was very tired.

Tick **one** box.

Overall stopping distance would be shorter. ☐   Only braking distance would be longer. ☐

Overall stopping distance would be longer. ☐   Only thinking distance would be longer. ☐

(1 mark)

2 Explain how human reaction time is related to the brain.

> **Guided**

Human reaction time is the time taken between a stimulus and ....

....

It is related to how quickly the human brain ....

.... **(2 marks)**

3 (a) Explain how to measure human reaction times using a ruler.

> Human reaction time can be measured using the 'drop test'.

....

....

....

....

....

.... **(4 marks)**

(b) Give the range of reaction times of an average person to an external stimulus.

.... **(1 mark)**

(c) Explain what you would expect to find when comparing the distance measured on the ruler, during a drop test, for a person with a reaction time of 0.2 s with that of a person with a reaction time of 0.9 s.

....

....

.... **(2 marks)**

Extended response – Forces

A skydiver leaves the training aeroplane and accelerates before opening the parachute. After opening the parachute, the speed of the skydiver reduces significantly so that he lands safely.

Explain the forces acting on the skydiver before and after opening the parachute and suggest a reason for the skydiver being in the position shown in the photograph. You should try to use the information given in the question.

You will be more successful in extended response questions if you plan your answer before you start writing. The question asks you to give a detailed explanation of the forces acting on the skydiver from the time he leaves the aeroplane. Think about:

- the forces acting on the skydiver causing him to accelerate
- how the forces change during the descent
- the effect of air resistance
- the effect of change in surface area
- the effect of balanced forces
- how the skydiver is able to land at a safe velocity.

You should try to use the information given in the question.

....

....

....

....

....

....

....

....

....

....

....

....

....

.... **(6 marks)**

Waves

1 Describe evidence that it is energy in a wave that travels, not the particles themselves, for ripples on the surface of water.

....

....

.... **(2 marks)**

2 Describe the difference between longitudinal and transverse waves.

....

....

.... **(2 marks)**

3 The diagram below shows a wave travelling through a medium.

Height of wave in cm

Note that both axes have units of cm.

Distance from source in cm

(a) Identify the correct amplitude of the wave in the diagram.

Tick **one** box.

0.05 m ☐   0.025 m ☐   0.12 m ☐   0.10 m ☐   **(1 mark)**

(b) Determine the wavelength of the wave in the diagram.

....

Wavelength = ... m **(1 mark)**

(c) Sketch a second wave on the diagram to show a higher amplitude and shorter wavelength than that of the wave shown. **(2 marks)**

(d) Determine the time period T of the wave if the speed of the wave is 3×10^8 m/s.

> **Guided**

You will need to recall the equation $v = f\lambda$ as it is not on the Physics Equation Sheet.
You will need to select the equation: period = 1 / frequency from the Physics Equation Sheet.

First find the frequency of the wave ....

.... **(2 marks)**

Then find the time period of the wave ....

.... **(2 marks)**

Wave equation

1 A sound wave has a wavelength of 0.017 m and a frequency of 20 000 Hz.

Calculate the speed of the wave.

....

....

Wave speed = ... m/s **(2 marks)**

2 Blue whales communicate over long distances by sending sound waves through the oceans.

ided

(a) If the speed of the sound through water is 1500 m/s, calculate the frequency of one note with a wavelength of 88 m produced by a blue whale.

Using $v = f\lambda$ rearrange the equation to give f = ...

....

....

Frequency = ... Hz **(2 marks)**

(b) If the note sent from another whale had a different frequency of 22 Hz, show that the wavelength of this note would also change from the wavelength in (a).

....

....

Wavelength = ... m **(2 marks)**

3 An icicle is melting into a pool of water. Drops fall every half a second, producing small waves that travel across the water at 0.05 m/s.

Calculate the wavelength of the small waves.

Select the correct unit from the box below.

seconds	hertz	metres

Remember to write down the equation that you are using before you substitute values.

....

....

....

Wavelength = ... unit .... **(3 marks)**

Measuring wave velocity

1 A tap is dripping into a bath. Three drops fall each second, producing small waves that are 5 cm apart.

Calculate the speed of the small waves across the water.

Select the correct unit from the box below.

m/s^2	m/s	m

The frequency of the waves (f) = ...

The wavelength of the waves (λ) = ...

....

Speed of waves = ... unit .... **(3 marks)**

2 Identify the distance between the crests of water waves with a frequency of 0.25 Hz travelling at a speed of 2 m/s.

Tick **one** box.

0.5 m   ☐

0.125 m   ☐

4 m   ☐

8 m   ☐

> You will find the equation $v = f\lambda$ useful. You will need to select this equation from the Physics Equation Sheet.

(1 mark)

3 An oscilloscope screen shows a waveform.

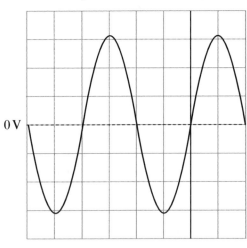

0 V

> You will find the equation period = 1 / frequency useful. You will need to select this equation from the Physics Equation Sheet.

Each division in the horizontal direction is 5 milliseconds.

Calculate the frequency of the wave.

....

....

....

Frequency = ... Hz **(3 marks)**

Practical skills

Required practical – Waves in fluids

1 A ripple tank is used to investigate waves.

(a) Describe how a ripple tank may be used to measure the frequency of water waves.

....

....

.... **(2 marks)**

(b) Describe how to find the wavelength of the waves in the ripple tank.

....

....

.... **(2 marks)**

(c) Give the equation you can use with the data collected in (a) and (b) to determine wave speed.

.... **(1 mark)**

(d) Identify the control variable when using a ripple tank to investigate wave speed.

.... **(1 mark)**

2 Describe a suitable conclusion to the method of using the ripple tank in question 1. Your conclusion should include two factors that should be moderated in this experiment.

Guided

A ripple tank can be used to determine a value for ....

....

.... **(3 marks)**

3 The ripple tank experiment uses several pieces of equipment. Complete the table below to describe the hazard associated with each component and suggest a measure to minimise the risk of harm.

> Identify the hazard and describe the safety measure for each mark.

Component	Hazard	Safety measure
water		
electricity		
strobe lamp		

(3 marks)

Waves and boundaries

1 (a) Identify which of the following will reflect the greatest amount of sound energy in air.

Tick **one** box.

hedge ☐   smooth stone wall ☐

wooden fence ☐   curtain ☐   **(1 mark)**

(b) Explain your answer to (a).

....

....

.... **(2 marks)**

2 Describe how a periscope works by referring to the simplified diagram. Include the following terms in your answer: angle of incidence, plane, angle of reflection, perpendicular, normal.

> **Guided**

Light waves from an object on the surface are reflected at a plane surface. The

angle of incidence equals the ....

....

....

....

.... **(4 marks)**

3 Draw and label a ray diagram to show what happens when a ray of light is reflected off a mirror.

mirror   **(3 marks)**

Practical skills

Required practical – Investigating refraction

1 (a) Suggest a method that could be used to investigate the refraction of light using a glass block and a ray box.

....

....

....

....

....

....

.... **(5 marks)**

(b) Explain what conclusion you would expect to find using the method you have outlined in (a). Your answer should refer to the angle of incidence and the angle of refraction.

When a light ray travels from air into a glass block ....

....

.... **(2 marks)**

(c) (i) Explain what would be observed if the light ray, travelling through the air, entered the glass at an angle of 90° to the surface of the glass.

.... **(1 mark)**

(ii) Explain what would be happening that could not be observed in this experiment.

....

....

.... **(2 marks)**

2 Give **three** hazards and appropriate safety measures that should be considered when investigating reflection using a mains-powered ray box.

....

....

....

....

.... **(3 marks)**

3 The refraction of light waves through transparent materials can be modelled using a ripple tank.

Describe what changes you would expect to observe in the waves when the depth of the water is made shallower by placing a glass sheet at an angle to the waves.

| Consider the waves being generated in deeper water and then moving into shallower water. |

....

....

....

.... **(2 marks)**   **79**

Electromagnetic spectrum

1 Visible and infrared radiation are given out by a candle. Gamma-rays are emitted by radioactive elements such as radium.

(a) Give **two** similarities between all waves in the electromagnetic spectrum.

Guided

All waves of the electromagnetic spectrum are .... waves

and they all travel .... **(2 marks)**

(b) Give an example that shows the transfer of energy by electromagnetic waves. Include the type of electromagnetic wave in your answer.

....

.... **(1 mark)**

2 The chart below represents the electromagnetic spectrum. Some types of electromagnetic radiation have been labelled.

longest wavelength/
lowest frequency

shortest wavelength/
highest frequency

←——— radio waves ———►◄—C—►◄infrared►B   ◄—►◄——A——►

ultra-
violet
rays (UV)

◄gamma►
rays

(a) Name the three parts of the spectrum that have been replaced by letters in the diagram.

A: ....

B: ....

C: .... **(3 marks)**

(b) Describe how frequency changes from radio waves to gamma-rays and how this is related to energy. Refer to these two types of radiation in your answer.

....

....

....

....

.... **(3 marks)**

3 The speed of electromagnetic waves in a vacuum is 300 000 000 km/s. A radio wave has a wavelength of 240 m. Calculate the frequency of the radio wave.

You will need to remember the equation $v = f\lambda$ because it's not on the Physics Equation Sheet.

....

....

....

Frequency = ... Hz **(2 marks)**

Required practical – Infrared radiation

1 (a) Describe an experimental method, using the apparatus in the diagram below, to investigate the radiation of thermal energy.

> The diagram shows a Leslie's Cube which has four different sides – dull black, shiny black, white, silver – and can be filled with hot liquid.

....

....

....

.... **(4 marks)**

Guided (b) Identify the independent and dependent variables in this experiment.

The dependent variable is temperature.

The independent variable is...

.... **(2 marks)**

(c) Give **four** control variables in this experiment.

....

.... **(2 marks)**

2 (a) Identify a hazard with using Leslie's cube.

.... **(1 mark)**

(b) Explain how the hazard can be minimised.

.... **(1 mark)**

3 Conical flasks covered with different coloured foils and containing cold water may be used to investigate the absorption of thermal energy, by heating them with a radiant heater placed at a measured distance from the flasks.

(a) Suggest a reason why the conical flasks should be fitted with bungs before starting the experiment.

.... **(1 mark)**

(b) Describe what you would expect to find at the end of the experiment for:

(i) dull and black surfaces

.... **(1 mark)**

(ii) shiny and light surfaces.

.... **(1 mark)**

Dangers and uses

1 Give **two** uses for each of the following EM waves.

(a) infrared waves:

1 .... 2 .... **(1 mark)**

(b) ultraviolet waves:

1 .... 2 .... **(1 mark)**

(c) gamma-rays:

1 .... 2 .... **(1 mark)**

(d) Give a use for microwaves other than for cooking.

.... **(1 mark)**

2 Medical X-rays are used to diagnose certain types of medical problems. The numbers of X-rays are carefully recorded.

Medical X-rays	Adult approximate effective radiation dose	Equivalent time of exposure to background radiation
radiography – chest	0.1 mSv	10 days
oral	0.005 mSv	1 day
computed tomography (CT) – lung cancer screening	1.5 mSv	6 months

(a) Using data from the table, compare the medical X-ray doses with background radiation.

....

....

....

....

....

.... **(3 marks)**

(b) Suggest why it is important to record and control the number of X-rays that a person has.

X-rays carry high amounts of energy.

....

....

....

.... **(2 marks)**

3 Describe the dangers of ultraviolet radiation.

....

....

....

.... **(2 marks)**

Lenses

1 Describe the main difference between the way converging and diverging lenses bend light.

A converging lens bends the rays of light towards each other. A diverging lens

bends the .... **(2 marks)**

2 The diagram below shows two lenses.

(a) Complete the diagrams for both
    lenses by drawing the rays to
    converge at a focal point.

lens 1

lens 2   **(4 marks)**

(b) Name the type of lens shown in the diagram.

.... **(1 mark)**

3 The symbol on the right represents a concave lens.

Remember that concave and convex
lenses can be represented by symbols.

(a) Draw three rays to show how light passes through the lens, then label the focal
    point and the focal length.   **(4 marks)**

(b) (i) Name the type of image you would expect to be formed by the concave lens.

.... **(1 mark)**

    (ii) Explain the reasons for your answer to (b)(i).

....

.... **(2 marks)**

4 (a) Explain how the focal point of a lens is related to its thickness.

....

.... **(2 marks)**

(b) Describe how the focal length of a lens is identified.

.... **(1 mark)**

Real and virtual images

Guided

1 Lenses refract light to form images, some of which can be seen on a screen. Explain the difference between a real image and a virtual image.

A real image is an image that can be projected ....

but a virtual image ....

A virtual image is produced when ....

.... **(3 marks)**

2 Add the following points to the diagram:

> You will need to use your ruler.

(a) 2F on each side of the lens.   **(1 mark)**

(b) The second focal point.   **(1 mark)**

(c) Arrow showing the position and type of image.   **(1 mark)**

3 A fossil measuring 3.3 mm is examined under a magnifying lens with a magnification of 4.5. Calculate the height of the resultant image of the fossil. Use the correct equation from the Physics Equation Sheet. Show your calculations.

> You will find this equation useful:
> $$\text{magnification} = \frac{\text{image height}}{\text{object height}}$$

....

....

.... **(2 marks)**

4 The table below shows the type of image produced by a converging lens when an object is placed at different points from the lens.

Position of object	Position of image	Type of image	Magnification	Upright/ inverted
closer than F	in front of lens	virtual	magnified	upright
between F and 2F	beyond 2F on the opposite side of the lens	real	magnified	inverted
at 2F	at 2F on the opposite side of the lens	real	same size	inverted
beyond 2F	F to 2F on the opposite side of the lens	real	smaller	inverted

(a) Describe what happens to the magnification of the image as the object gets closer to the focal point from 2F.

.... **(1 mark)**

(b) Give the point at which the image changes to a virtual image.

.... **(1 mark)**

(c) Give the point at which the image is real and the same size as the object.

.... **(1 mark)**

Visible light

1 Identify the correct categories of materials that transmit light.

Tick **one** box.

opaque and transparent ☐

opaque and translucent ☐

translucent and transparent ☐

transparent only ☐   **(1 mark)**

2 Give an example of where specular reflection occurs.

.... **(1 mark)**

3 Explain why an opaque green object appears green in white light.

An opaque green object appears green because ....

....

and all other colours .... **(2 marks)**

4 Suggest a scientific principle to explain the following statements about coloured light.

(a) Violet light carries more energy than red light.

....

.... **(1 mark)**

(b) A green book cover with a blue title under white light, is seen as a green book cover with a black title when placed under yellow light.

....

....

.... **(3 marks)**

5 Describe, with the aid of a diagram, how diffuse reflection still obeys the law of reflection even though light is scattered.

Remember that reflection from a rough surface causes scattering.

....

....

....

....

.... **(5 marks)**

Black body radiation

1 A hot cup of coffee is left on the table and cools down. Which statement explains why this happens?

Tick **one** box.

The cup absorbs more radiation than it emits. ☐

The cup emits more radiation than it absorbs. ☐

The cup emits the same amount of radiation as it absorbs. ☐

Radiation is transferred from the surroundings. ☐   **(1 mark)**

2 Two cups of coffee are left at the same time to cool down. The starting temperature for Cup A is 80 °C and the starting temperature for Cup B is 55 °C. Explain which cup will radiate the most heat in 5 minutes.

....

....

.... **(2 marks)**

3 Explain the term 'perfect black body' in terms of the absorption and emission of radiation.

> **Guided**

A perfect black body is an object that ....

all of the .... incident on it. A black body does not

....

....

.... **(3 marks)**

4 Astronomers can analyse the temperature of stars by examining the wavelengths and intensity of light that the stars emit. Describe how astronomers can use these data to determine the temperature of a star.

....

....

....

....

....

....

.... **(2 marks)**

Extended response – Waves

X-rays and gamma-rays are widely used in a number of applications. Compare the characteristics and properties of these waves and give examples of how they can be used safely in medical diagnosis and in industry.

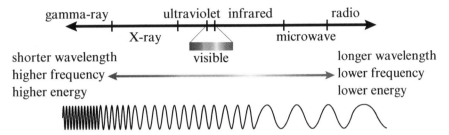

You will be more successful in extended response questions if you plan your answer before you start writing.

The question asks you to give a detailed explanation of the properties, uses and dangers of X-rays and gamma-rays. Think about:

- the types of radiation and how you would describe them

- the dangers of both types of radiation and the reasons why they can be dangerous

- examples of how the two types of radiation are used in medicine

- examples of how the two types of radiation are used in industry.

You should try to use the information given in the question and in the diagram.

....
....
....
....
....
....
....
....
....
....
....
....
....
....
....
.... **(6 marks)**

Magnets and magnetic fields

1 Complete the diagram below to show the magnetic field lines for a bar magnet.

> Remember to consider the relative density of the field lines as well as their direction. You should show at least 10 magnetic field lines to represent the field.

(4 marks)

2 Write down **three** similarities between the magnetic field of a bar magnet and that produced by the Earth.

> **Guided**

A bar magnet and the Earth both have ....

A bar magnet and the Earth have similar ....

The direction of both fields can be found using .... (3 marks)

3 An electric doorbell uses an induced magnet to move the hammer, which then rings the bell when the switch is pressed.

Explain why an induced magnet rather than a permanent magnet is used for this application.

....

....

....

....

....

.... (5 marks)

Current and magnetism

1 The diagrams below show a wire passing through a circular card. The **cross** represents the conventional current moving into the page and the **dot** represents the conventional current moving out of the page.

(a)   (b)

(a) Draw magnetic field lines on each diagram to show the **pattern** of the magnetic field. **(2 marks)**

(b) Draw arrows on each diagram to show the **direction** of the magnetic field. **(2 marks)**

(c) Describe how the magnetic field around the wire can be increased.

....

.... **(1 mark)**

2 (a) Identify which of the following has a magnetic field similar in shape to that of a solenoid, as shown in the diagram below.

Tick **one** box.

ball magnet   ☐

bar magnet   ☐

circular magnet   ☐

horseshoe magnet ☐   **(1 mark)**

magnetic field

coil carrying electric current

(b) Describe how the magnetic field of the solenoid shown in the diagram in (a) can be made stronger, without changing the circuit.

....

.... **(1 mark)**

3 Give **three** factors that affect the force acting on a current-carrying wire in a magnetic field.

The force acting on a current-carrying wire in a magnetic field depends on the

.... of the wire, the .... in the wire and the

.... **(3 marks)**

Guided

Extended response – Magnetism and electromagnetism

Describe how an experiment could show the effect and strength of a magnetic field around a long straight conductor and what would be observed when the circuit was connected.

> You will be more successful in extended response questions if you plan your answer before you start writing.
>
> The question asks you to give a detailed explanation of the magnetic field generated by a long straight conductor. Think about:
>
> - how you would safely connect the conductor to enable circuit measurements to be taken
> - the methods you could use to determine the direction of a magnetic field
> - the shape of the magnetic field that you would expect to find
> - how you would interpret the field patterns of long straight conductors
> - the variable that would influence the strength of the magnetic field around a long straight conductor
> - how the influence of the magnetic field of a long straight conductor changes.
>
> You should try to use the information given in the question.

....

....

....

....

....

....

....

....

....

....

....

....

....

....

....

....

....

....

.... **(6 marks)**

Had a go ☐   Nearly there ☐   Nailed it! ☐

The Solar System

1 Name the main components of the Solar System.

| S.......................... | p.......................... | d.......................... | m.......................... |

(1 mark)

2 Explain the difference between a planet and a moon.

....

.... **(2 marks)**

3 (a) Describe a difference between the Milky Way and the Solar System in terms of stars.

The Solar System has only ....

but the Milky Way contains .... **(2 marks)**

(b) Describe another difference between the Solar System and the Milky Way.

The Solar System is a simple ....

but the Milky Way is a .... **(2 marks)**

4 (a) Name the **two** types of planets that exist in the Solar System.

1. ....

2. .... **(2 marks)**

(b) Identify the planet in the list below that is a different type from the other three.

Tick **one** box.

Mercury ☐   Saturn ☐

Mars ☐   Venus ☐   **(1 mark)**

(c) Give a reason for your answer to (b).

.... **(1 mark)**

(d) Describe the difference between the Earth and Neptune in terms of their surface and atmosphere.

....

....

.... **(2 marks)**

(e) How was Pluto originally classified?

.... **(1 mark)**

(f) How is Pluto now classified?

.... **(1 mark)**

The life cycle of stars

1 Name the process that occurs in a star when hydrogen nuclei combine to form helium nuclei.

.... **(1 mark)**

2 Identify the force that draws a cloud of gas and dust together at the start of a star's life cycle.

Tick **one** box.

friction   ☐   reaction   ☐

gravity   ☐   air resistance ☐   **(1 mark)**

3 The flow chart below shows the different stages in the evolution of stars with masses similar to the Sun, and of stars with masses much bigger than that of the Sun.

Complete the diagram using words from the box. You do not need to use all of the words.

| black | dwarf | electron | giant | hole | neutron |
| proton | protostar | supergiant | supernova | white |

(4 marks)

Cloud of gas and dust (nebula)

....

Stars much bigger than the Sun

Main sequence star

Stars about the same size as the Sun

Red ....

....

Red ....

....

.... star   Black ....

Black ....

4 Describe how all elements in the periodic table are linked to star processes in the universe.

> **Guided**

Consider how fusion processes have led to the formation of elements and how they have been distributed throughout the universe.

All of the naturally occurring elements in the periodic table are produced by

....

Elements heavier than .... are produced in ....

These explosions of .... then distribute the

elements .... **(5 marks)**

Satellites and orbits

1 Moons that orbit planets are also known by which other name?

Tick **one** box.

artificial satellites ☐

asteroids ☐

dwarf planets ☐

natural satellites ☐   **(1 mark)**

2 Explain the difference between the orbit of
a planet and the orbit of a moon.

> Our Solar System is an example of a star that has
> its own planets, most with their own moons.

....

....

....

.... **(2 marks)**

3 (a) Give the name of the force that allows satellites to maintain their orbits.

.... **(1 mark)**

(b) The orbits of artificial satellites around the Earth can be classified into two main types.

(i) Give the two types of orbits of artificial satellites.

....

.... **(1 mark)**

(ii) Give an example of each type of satellite.

....

.... **(2 marks)**

4 (a) Suggest a similarity in the orbit of planets, moons and satellites.

uided Planets, moons and artificial satellites all move in .... orbits. **(1 mark)**

(b) Suggest a difference between the orbit of the Moon and that of an artificial satellite.

A moon orbits at a .... from its planet but the orbit of an

artificial satellite can be changed by adjusting its ....

and the .... of its orbit.   **(3 marks)**

Red-shift

1 Identify the observation made when light is red-shifted.

Tick **one** box.

the light waves travel faster ☐   light is expanding ☐

the frequency increases ☐   the wavelength increases ☐   **(1 mark)**

Guided

2 The diagram shows light from the Sun and light from a distant galaxy. Describe how evidence from a galaxy, observed to have a red-shifted spectrum, gives evidence that the universe is expanding.

sun

★

◉

distant
galaxy   400   500   600   700

A galaxy with a red-shifted spectrum indicates that the galaxy is ....

.... The further the black lines are shifted

.... As most galaxies are red-shifted

this would suggest .... **(3 marks)**

3 The observation of red-shift has enabled scientists to build and develop models to try to understand the evolution, scale and structure of the universe.

(a) Name the model that scientists have developed, from their observations of red-shift, to explain the origin of the universe.

.... **(1 mark)**

(b) Distant galaxies are thought to be moving away (receding) faster than the closer galaxies. Describe what type of observation led scientists to this conclusion.

....

.... **(2 marks)**

(c) Describe what observations of the expanding universe might suggest about its origin.

....

.... **(2 marks)**

(d) (i) Give the names of what appear to bend light and hold galaxies together but cannot be detected by electromagnetic radiation.

....

.... **(2 marks)**

(ii) Describe what may be happening to the expansion of the universe and why it is so difficult to explain.

....

.... **(2 marks)**

Extended response – Space physics

The Big Bang theory is currently widely accepted as the best explanation of the origin of the universe. Explain why scientists currently accept the Big Bang theory and why it is referred to as the 'current best theory'.

> You will be more successful in extended response questions if you plan your answer before you start writing.
>
> The question asks you to give a detailed explanation of why scientists believe that the Big Bang theory provides the best explanation for the origins of the universe. Think about:
>
> - a description of what the universe was believed to have started from
> - what has happened since the start of the universe
> - the evidence that red-shift supplies in support of the Big Bang theory
> - a conclusion that can be reached as a result of red-shift observations
> - why scientists have been able to accept the Big Bang theory
> - observations that may cast doubt on the Big Bang theory.
>
> You should try to use the information given in the question.

....

....

....

....

....

....

....

....

....

....

....

....

....

....

....

....

....

.... **(6 marks)**

Timed Test 1

Time allowed: 1 hour 45 minutes

Total marks: 100

AQA publishes official Sample Assessment Material on its website. The Timed Test has been written to help you practise what you have learned and may not be representative of a real exam paper.

1 (a) A scientist works in the countryside to investigate levels of radioactivity on a remote moor.

He uses a Geiger–Müller detector to measure the count rate.

The detector points across the countryside and the level recorded is an average of 25 counts per minute.

(i)   Name the radiation that the scientist is measuring.   **(1 mark)**

(ii) Give **two** sources of this radiation.   **(2 marks)**

(iii) Suggest why the scientist takes a number of readings and then calculates an average.   **(1 mark)**

(b) The scientist conducts a second experiment in the laboratory. First, he measures the background radiation only. Then he tests a sample of radioactive material. He removes the readings for background radiation from those taken from the radioactive sample and records the corrected count rate in a table.

Time in minutes	Corrected count rate in counts / min
0	1030
1	760
2	515
3	387
4	258
5	194
6	129
7	98
8	65

(i)   Plot a graph of the corrected count rate against time.   **(3 marks)**

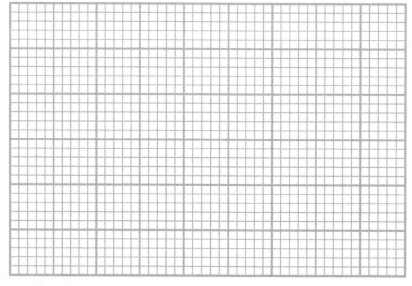

(ii) Add a curve of best fit.   **(1 mark)**

(iii) Determine the half-life of the radioactive source.   **(1 mark)**

(c) Describe the nature of alpha, beta and gamma radiation in terms of ionising properties.   **(3 marks)**

2 A lift travels between floors in a building.

(a) The lift moves from the ground floor to the fourth floor through a height of 15 m in 20 s. The mass of the lift is 750 kg.

    (i) Calculate how much energy the lift gains in moving from the ground floor to the fourth floor. Take g to be 10 N/kg. **(2 marks)**

    (ii) Calculate the average power that the elevator exerts in moving the mass of 750 kg to the fourth floor. Choose the correct unit from the box.

W	N	J

(3 marks)

(b) As the lift moves upwards, not all of the energy supplied is usefully transferred. Suggest where some of the wasted energy is transferred to. **(1 mark)**

(c) Calculate the kinetic energy of the elevator in moving from the ground floor to the fourth floor. **(4 marks)**

(d) Explain why this mechanical process could be described as wasteful. **(2 marks)**

(e) Give an example of wasted energy in the process described in (d). **(1 mark)**

3 (a) A kettle is rated at 2000 W and is designed to operate on a 230 V mains supply.

    (i) Write the equation that links power, voltage and current. **(1 mark)**

    (ii) Calculate the current drawn by the kettle. **(2 marks)**

    (iii) Describe what could happen to the kettle if a fuse were to be fitted that has:

    too high a rating **(1 mark)**

    too low a rating. **(1 mark)**

    (iv) Which fuse should be fitted to the kettle to make it safe?

    Tick **one** box.

    1 A ☐   3 A ☐   10 A ☐   13 A ☐ **(1 mark)**

(b) Calculate the charge moved in the kettle in (a) each second. Choose the correct unit from the box.

C	J	W

(3 marks)

4 An electrical heater supplies electrical energy to a copper block of mass 2000 g at 12 V with a current of 12 A for 2 minutes.

(a) Calculate the energy supplied to the heater. Use the correct equation from the Physics Equation Sheet. Choose the correct unit from the box.

J	A	V

(3 marks)

(b) Calculate the temperature rise for the block of copper when supplied with 2880 J. The specific heat capacity of copper is 385 J/kg °C. Use the correct equation from the Physics Equation Sheet. Choose the correct unit from the box.

J	°C	W

(3 marks)

(c) Suggest why the actual temperature rise may be lower than the predicted value. **(1 mark)**

(d) (i) Explain how unwanted energy transfer in the heating of a metal block could be reduced. **(1 mark)**

    (ii) Name the type of material that should be used to reduce thermal energy transfer. **(1 mark)**

5 (a) (i) Complete the nuclear equation below.

$$_{91}^{.....}\text{Pa} \rightarrow {}_{.....}^{227}\text{Ac} + {}_{.....}^{4}\text{He}$$

(1 mark)

    (ii) Name the type of decay in (i). **(1 mark)**

(b) (i) Complete the nuclear equation below.

$$_{87}^{....}Fr \rightarrow \, _{2}^{....}He + _{....}^{207}At$$

(1 mark)

   (ii) Name the type of decay in (i).   (1 mark)

(c) (i) Complete the nuclear equation below.

$$_{11}^{24}Na \rightarrow \, _{....}^{24}Mg + _{-1}^{....}e$$

(1 mark)

   (ii) Name the type of decay in (i).   (1 mark)

(d) (i) Complete the nuclear equation below.

$$_{....}^{201}Au \rightarrow \, _{80}^{....}Hg + _{-1}^{0}e$$

(1 mark)

   (ii) Name the type of decay in (i).   (1 mark)

(e) (i) Name any changes that occur as a result of alpha nuclear decay in terms of mass and charge.   (1 mark)

   (ii) Name any changes that occur as a result of beta nuclear decay in terms of mass and charge.   (1 mark)

6 A stationary fuel tanker delivers fuel to a plane. The fuel line is connected to an earth wire to prevent any static charge building up.

   (a) (i) Explain why static electricity may build up in the fuel line.   (2 marks)

      (ii) Explain why the build-up of static charge could be dangerous in this situation.   (2 marks)

   (b) Explain the role of the earth wire attached to the fuel line.   (2 marks)

   (c) Discuss how an electric field may be generated and the effect that this may have on a charged object within that field. Include a diagram to illustrate the electric field generated from a positive point source.   (6 marks)

7 The circuit diagram shows three identical lamps and one cell.

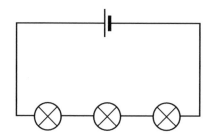

(a) The cell provides 1.5 V. Explain what the potential difference across each lamp is.   (2 marks)

(b) Add a voltmeter to the circuit diagram to show how you could measure the potential difference across one lamp.   (1 mark)

(c) Name **one** component that could be added to make the lamps brighter.   (1 mark)

(d) Suggest a more effective way of connecting the lamps to make them brighter.   (1 mark)

(e) The circuit diagram below shows a circuit to test a thermistor.

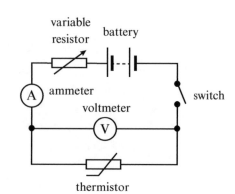

   (i) Describe how resistance changes in a thermistor.

                     (3 marks)

   (ii) Give a use for a thermistor in a domestic circuit.

                     (1 mark)

8 (a) Draw diagrams in the boxes to show the differences in particle arrangement for elements of solids, liquids and gases.   **(2 marks)**

| solid | liquid | gas |

(b) Explain the difference between solids, liquids and gases in terms of the kinetic energy of particles.   **(6 marks)**

9 (a) A student conducts an investigation into density. She measures the dimensions of three blocks with a ruler to calculate the volume. The first block has a volume of 0.2 m^3 and a mass of 1500 g. The second block has a volume of 0.15 m^3 and a mass of 0.7 kg. The third block has a volume of 0.2 m^3 and a mass of 0.7 kg. Determine which block has the highest density.

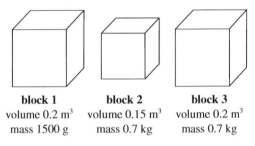

block 1	block 2	block 3
volume 0.2 m^3	volume 0.15 m^3	volume 0.2 m^3
mass 1500 g	mass 0.7 kg	mass 0.7 kg

(4 marks)

(b) The student now investigates the density of three irregular rocks. She fills a Eureka can with water, places the first rock into the can and collects the water displaced in a measuring cylinder.

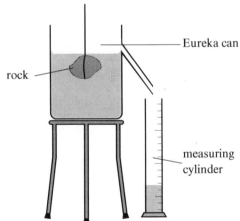

(i) Explain what the student must do to make sure that the reading on the measuring cylinder is as accurate as possible.   **(2 marks)**

(ii) Describe the other measurement that the student must make to be able to calculate the density of the rock.   **(2 marks)**

10 (a) Describe the differences between Thomson's model of the atom (the 'plum pudding' model) and Rutherford's model of the atom (the 'nuclear' model).   **(4 marks)**

(b) Describe the alpha-scattering experiment, carried out by Geiger and Marsden, which produced evidence to suggest and support a new model for the atom.   **(6 marks)**

Timed Test 2

Time allowed: 1 hour 45 minutes

Total marks: 100

AQA publishes official Sample Assessment Material on its website. The Timed Test has been written to help you practise what you have learned and may not be representative of a real exam paper.

1 Two students plan to set up an experiment to measure speed. They have a trolley, an inclined ramp, a ruler and a stopwatch.

   (a) Describe a method that they could use to measure the speed of the trolley using the apparatus above. **(4 marks)**

   (b) Suggest other apparatus that the students could use to improve the precision of the data collected. **(2 marks)**

   (c) The students then extended their experiment to investigate the effect of the independent variable. The table below shows data collected by the students.

1	2	3	4
in cm	in m	in s	in [unit]
5	1.80	3.2	
10	1.80	2.4	
15	1.80	1.8	
20	1.80	1.4	
25	1.80	1.0	
30	1.80	0.4	
35	1.80	0.2	

   (i)   Suggest what the independent variable is. **(1 mark)**

   (ii) Write titles for columns 1–3 in the table. **(1 mark)**

   (iii) Write a heading in column 4 that would be useful for recording processed data. Give the unit. **(1 mark)**

   (d) After travelling down the ramp, the trolley comes to a stop by itself.

   (i)   Describe the forces that cause the trolley to stop. **(2 marks)**

   (ii) Describe how these forces could be reduced. **(2 marks)**

2 A test car of mass 1000 kg is driven at the design testing centre to examine braking forces. The car starts from rest and accelerates to its final speed.

   (a) Give the quantities that need to be known in order to calculate the acceleration of the car. **(2 marks)**

   (b) The car accelerates from rest to a speed of 10 m/s in a time of 20 s. Calculate the acceleration of the car. **(2 marks)**

   (c) Calculate how far the car will travel in the time given in (b). **(3 marks)**

3 (a) Which stage is **not** part of the life cycle of a star of similar mass to the Sun?

   Tick **one** box.

   main sequence ☐   supernova ☐

   nebula ☐   white dwarf ☐   **(1 mark)**

   (b) (i) Define the term 'nuclear fusion'. **(1 mark)**

(ii) Describe the **two** outcomes of fusion processes in stars relating to naturally occurring elements. **(2 marks)**

(iii) Describe how supernovae play a role in the production and distribution of elements. **(2 marks)**

4 The diagram below shows the graph of a radio wave.

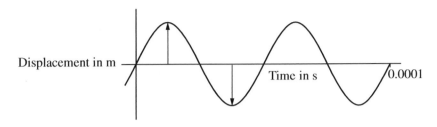

(a) (i) Give the equation linking time period and frequency. **(1 mark)**

(ii) Identify the time period of the wave by adding 'T' with arrows to indicate one complete time period. **(1 mark)**

(iii) Calculate the frequency of the wave shown in the diagram. **(3 marks)**

(b) Using the diagram of the wave, explain each of the following terms:

(i) amplitude **(1 mark)**

(ii) wavelength **(1 mark)**

(iii) frequency **(1 mark)**

(c) Sound waves and water waves are two different types of wave. Give the **two** types of wave. **(1 mark)**

5 (a) Give the property of light that enables it to be used in fibre optic communications. **(1 mark)**

(b) The diagram shows a light wave being refracted through a glass block.

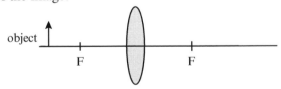

(i) Label the angle of incidence (*i*) and the angle of refraction (*r*) on the diagram. **(2 marks)**

(ii) Explain what the 'normal' is on the diagram and why it is drawn. **(2 marks)**

(c) Light entering a convex lens is shown in the diagram. Complete the diagram to show the location and orientation of the image. **(3 marks)**

6 Edwin Hubble discovered that light from galaxies that was seen from Earth was red-shifted. He found this by looking at the absorption spectra of stars and galaxies.

(a) Describe how the characteristics of a light source that is red-shifted are different from light that is not red-shifted. **(2 marks)**

(b) Suggest the relationship between the recessional speed of galaxies in relation to the observed wavelength of their light. **(2 marks)**

(c) Explain how the observations of red-shift provide evidence for the Big Bang model of the universe. **(2 marks)**

(d) Scientists have observed massive objects in the universe that have helped to develop the idea of red-shift. Explain what these objects are and how they are linked to red-shift. **(3 marks)**

(e) Red-shift alone does not fully explain the Big Bang model of the universe. Describe the other piece of evidence that supports this model. **(2 marks)**

(f) Astronomers think that galaxies should rotate much faster than they do. Describe the ideas that scientists have proposed that may account for this and why they cannot be explained. **(3 marks)**

7 The Solar System is a collection of many bodies that orbit round other bodies in space.

(a) Give the name of the force that keeps planets and moons in their orbits. **(1 mark)**

(b) Explain the difference between the orbits of planets, including dwarf planets, and the orbits of moons. **(2 marks)**

(c) Most planets of the Solar System have natural satellites. Compare Jupiter with Mars in terms of relative planetary size and relative number of natural satellites. **(2 marks)**

(d) Explain why a satellite can have a constant speed but a changing velocity. **(2 marks)**

(e) Describe the life cycle of a star like our Sun, which is the centre of our Solar System. **(6 marks)**

8 The diagram shows a wire passing through a card. A compass is placed in different spots around the wire to determine the direction of the magnetic field.

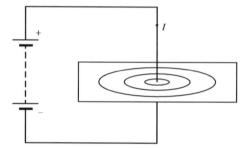

(a) (i) Draw arrows on the diagram to show the magnetic field produced when the current flows through the coil. **(2 marks)**

  (ii) Name the rule that can be used to determine the direction of the field. **(1 mark)**

(b) (i) The wire is now turned into a solenoid. Draw the new magnetic field that is produced. **(4 marks)**

coil carrying
electric current

  (ii) Suggest a use for this device. **(1 mark)**

(c) Electromagnets used in scrapyards have an iron core in the coil. Explain why an iron core is used. **(2 marks)**

9 The diagram below shows part of the electromagnetic spectrum.

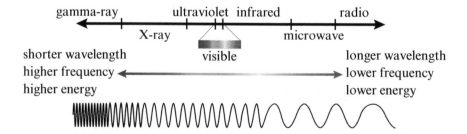

(a) Give one use for each of the following electromagnetic waves.

  (i) microwaves **(1 mark)**

  (ii) ultraviolet **(1 mark)**

  (iii) gamma-rays **(1 mark)**

(b) (i) Identify the correct term to classify electromagnetic (EM) waves.

Tick **one** box.

longitudinal ☐

mechanical ☐

seismic ☐

transverse ☐ **(1 mark)**

(ii) Describe **two** other similarities of all EM waves. **(2 marks)**

(c) A red jumper looks red in white light.

(i) Give the type of reflection that allows you to see the jumper. **(1 mark)**

(ii) Explain why the jumper looks red in white light. **(2 marks)**

(iii) Explain what colour the jumper would appear in blue light. **(2 marks)**

10 Two students carry out an experiment to investigate the extension of a spring. They add five masses to a spring: one 10 g mass, one 50 g mass and three 100 g masses. They then measure the final extension. When the spring is unloaded, the students find that the spring has stretched.

(a) Identify a problem with investigating inelastic deformation when using this method. **(1 mark)**

(b) Suggest **two** ways of improving the experiment. **(2 marks)**

(c) The table below shows results from a different experiment for the loading of a 32-mm spring. Complete the missing values in the table.

Weight in N	Extension in mm
0	32
0.1	
	40
0.3	
0.4	48
	52
0.6	56

(2 marks)

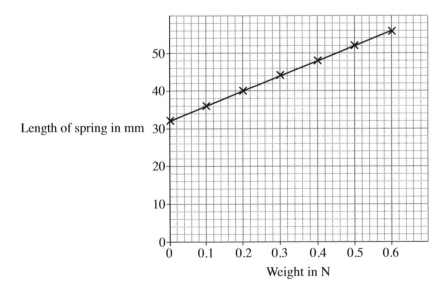

(d) Explain how the graph illustrates the relationship between the length of the spring and the weight added. You should refer to the graph in your answer. **(4 marks)**

Answers

Answers

Extended response questions

Answers to 6-mark questions are indicated with a star (*).
In your exam, your answers to 6-mark questions will be marked on how well you present and organise your response, not just on the scientific content. Your responses should contain most or all of the points given in the answers below, but you should also make sure that you show how the points link to each other, and structure your response in a clear and logical way.

1 Energy stores and systems

1 elastic potential **(1)**

2 A – gravitational, C – chemical, D – kinetic **(1)** (all three needed for mark)

3 (a) Store of chemical energy. **(1)**

   (b) Energy transfer by electrical current. **(1)**

   (c) Energy transfer to the surroundings by sound waves and by heating. **(1)** (both needed for mark)

4 The total energy available initially in this closed system, in the gravitational potential store, is 250 J **(1)**. As the basket reaches the ground, the gravitational potential store will become 0 J **(1)**, because it has been transferred to a total of 250 J of useful kinetic energy **(1)** and wasted thermal energy **(1)**.

2 Changes in energy

1 $E_p = mgh$ **(1)**

2 Kinetic energy $E_k = ½ mv^2 = 70$ m/s × (6 m/s)^2 **(3)**

3 Convert units: 15 cm = 0.15 m **(1)**

   Energy transferred $E = ½ k x^2 = ½ × 200$ N/m × (0.15 m)^2 **(1)** = 2.25 **(1)** J

4 Gravitational potential energy $(E_p) = 60$ kg × 10 N/kg × 0.7 m **(1)** = 420 **(1)** J

3 Energy changes in systems

1 Specific heat capacity = change in thermal energy / (mass × change in temperature) or $c = ΔE / (m × ΔT)$ **(1)**

2 $ΔE = m c Δθ$ **(1)** = 0.8 kg × 4200 J / kg °C × 50 °C **(1)** = 168 000 **(1)** J

3 $Δθ = ΔE / (m c)$ so $Δθ = 20 000$ J / (1.2 kg × 385 J/kg °C) **(1)** = 43 **(1)** so

   Change in temperature of the copper = 43 °C **(1)**

4 $ΔE = m c Δθ$ **(1)** so

   Specific heat capacity $c = 16 200$ J / (0.8 kg × 25 °C) **(1)** = 16 200/20 = 810 **(1)** J / kg °C

4 Required practical – Specific heat capacity

1 (a) the amount of energy required to raise the temperature of 1 kg of material by 1 K (or 1 °C) **(1)**

   (b) energy supplied, mass and change in temperature **(1)**

2 (a) Place a beaker on a balance, zero the balance and add a measured mass of water **(1)**. Take a start reading of the temperature **(1)**. Place the electrical heater into the water and switch on **(1)**. Take a temperature reading every 30 seconds **(1)** until the water reaches the required temperature **(1)**.

   (b) Measure the current supplied, the potential difference across the heater and the time for which the current is switched on **(1)**. Use these values to calculate the thermal energy supplied using the equation $E = V × I × t$ **(1)**.

   (c) Add insulation around the beaker **(1)** so less thermal energy is transferred to the surroundings and a more accurate value for the specific heat capacity of the water may be obtained **(1)**.

3 Plot a graph of temperature against time **(1)**. The changes of state are shown when the graph is horizontal (the temperature is not increasing) **(1)**.

5 Power

1 2500 W **(1)**

2 Energy transferred = 15 000 J, time taken = 20 s

   $P = E / t$

   so power $P = 15 000$ J / 20 s **(1)** = 750 **(1)** W

3 (a) $E_p = m g h$ so $E_p = 60 × 10 × (0.08 × 20)$ **(1)** = 960 **(1)** joules / J **(1)**

   (b) $P = E / t$ so $P = 960 / 12 = 80$ watts / W **(1)** (allow value for energy calculated in (a))

4 (a) For 3 W motor: $t = 360$ J / 3 W **(1)** = 180 **(1)** s

   (b) For 5 W motor: $t = 360$ J / 5 W **(1)** = 72 **(1)** s

6 Energy transfers and efficiency

1 (a) concrete **(1)**

   (b) Low relative thermal conductivity means that a material will have a slow **(1)** rate of transfer of thermal energy **(1)**.

2 (a) Thicker walls provide more material for the thermal energy **(1)** to travel through from the inside to outside, so the rate of thermal energy loss **(1)** is less, keeping the houses warmer.

   (b) Thicker walls provide more material for the thermal energy **(1)** to travel through from the outside to inside, so the rate of thermal energy transfer **(1)** is less, keeping the house cool.

3 rate of data collection **(1)**

4 The useful energy transferred to the box = 100 J; total energy transferred by the motor = 400 J; efficiency = 100 J / 400 J **(1)** = 0.25 **(1)** (accept × 100 = 25%)

7 Required practical – Thermal insulation

1 (a) Any **five** of the following points: select a minimum of four beakers, one to remain unwrapped as a control **(1)**, wrap three or more beakers with the same

mass / thickness of insulating material **(1)**, provide insulating bases and lids (with a hole for the thermometer) **(1)**, add the same amount of boiling or very hot water to the beakers **(1)**, place thermometers in each beaker and record the temperature of the water at the highest point **(1)**, start stop watch **(1)**, and if recording a temperature curve, take temperature reading every minute (or other suitable time increment) **(1)**.

   (b) independent variable – type of insulation selected **(1)**; dependent variable – temperature **(1)**

   (c) control variables: any four from – mass / thickness of insulating material, volume of water, starting temperature of the water, size of beaker, material of beaker, time of experiment (for four **(2)**, for three **(1)**)

2 Any one of the following: hot water in eyes can cause damage – always wear eye goggles **(1)**; hot water can cause scalds – place kettle close to beakers **(1)**; control beaker, and others, can cause burns – do not touch **(1)**; spilt water can cause slippage – report and wipe up **(1)**; glass thermometers can be broken and cause cuts – handle with care (same if using glass beakers) **(1)**.

3 A digital thermometer can improve accuracy in reading the temperature **(1)**.

4 The greater the thickness of insulating material, the slower the rate at which the hot water cools **(1)**. The lower the thermal conductivity of the insulating material, the lower the rate at which the hot water will cool **(1)**.

8 Energy resources

1 coal, oil and gas (any order) **(1)** (all three needed for mark)

2 (a) A hydroelectric power station is a reliable producer of electricity because it uses the gravitational potential energy of water which can be stored until it is needed **(1)**. As long as there is no prolonged drought / lack of rain the supply should be constant **(1)**.

   (b) Any **one** of the following: hydroelectric power stations have to be built in mountainous areas / high up (compared with supply areas, so that the gravitational potential energy can be captured) **(1)**; the UK has very few mountainous areas like this **(1)**; and limited to areas such as North Wales and Scottish Highlands **(1)**.

3 (a) When carbon dioxide is released into the atmosphere it contributes to the greenhouse effect / build-up of CO_2 **(1)** which is believed to contribute to global warming **(1)**.

(b) Sulfur dioxide and nitrogen oxides have been found to dissolve in the water droplets in rainclouds, increasing their acidity **(1)**; this can kill plants and forests / lakes or dissolve the surfaces of historical limestone buildings **(1)**.

(c) Any two from: Coal mines / oil / gas wells create environmental scars on the landscape **(1)**. Vehicles used to transport fossil fuels add to environmental pollution **(1)**. Alternative answers may include: Accidents in the extraction of oil from deep sea reserves can result in sea pollution **(1)**. New methods of extraction may impact on previously unused areas of the environment e.g. fracking **(1)**. Large transport networks may be needed to transport fuels **(1)**.

9 Patterns of energy use

1 (a)
1. After 1900, the world's energy demand rose / increased **(1)** as the population grew.
2. There was development in industry / demand in energy supply **(1)**.
3. The rise of power stations using fossil fuels added to demand **(1)**.

(b) (i) coal, oil and natural gas **(1)** (all three needed)

(ii) Any two from: population has increased so domestic energy use has increased **(1)**; industry has grown, requiring more energy **(1)**; vehicle use and travel have grown, requiring more energy **(1)** (and any other valid reason)

(iii) Nuclear research only began from the 1940s onwards **(1)**.

(iv) hydroelectric **(1)**

2 As the population continues to rise the demand for energy will also continue to rise **(1)**. Current trends show that the use of fossil fuels is the major contributor to the world's energy resources **(1)**. These are running out and no other energy resource has, so far, taken their place **(1)**. This could lead to a large gap between demand and supply **(1)**. (Any other valid reason)

10 Extended response – Energy

The answer should include some of the following points: **(6)**
- Refer to the change in gravitational potential energy (E_p) as the swing seat is pulled back / raised higher.
- Before release, the E_p is at maximum / kinetic energy (E_k) of the swing is at a minimum.
- When the swing is released, the E_p store falls and the E_k store increases.
- E_k is at a maximum at the mid-point, E_p is at a minimum.
- The system is not 100% efficient; some energy is dissipated to the environment.
- Friction due to air resistance and / or at the pivot results in the transfer of thermal energy to the surroundings / environment.
- Damping, due to friction, will result in the E_k being transferred to the thermal energy store of the swing and hence to the environment.

- Eventually all the E_p will have been dissipated to the surroundings / environment (so is no longer useful).

11 Circuit symbols

1 LDR **(1)**

2 (a) 1. resistor **(1)**
2. fuse **(1)**
3. variable resistor **(1)**

(b) fuse **(1)**

3

Component	Symbol	Purpose
ammeter		measures electric current
fixed resistor		provides a fixed resistance to the flow of current
diode		allows the current to flow one way only
switch	or	allows the current to be switched on / off

(Each correctly completed row gains 1 mark.)

4 Diagram showing series circuit diagram with battery / power supply **(1)**. Resistor **(1)** with ammeter in series **(1)**. Voltmeter connected in parallel across the resistor **(1)**.

12 Electrical charge and current

1 (a) An electric current is the rate **(1)** of flow of charge (electrons in a metal) **(1)**.

(b) Charge $Q = I t = 4 A \times 8 s$ **(1)** $= 32$ **(1)** coulombs / C **(1)**

2 (a) (i) The current is the same in all parts of a series circuit so the readings on ammeter 1 and ammeter 3 will be the same as that shown for ammeter 2 **(1)**.

(ii) Add another cell / increase the energy supplied **(1)**.

(b) cell **(1)**

3 (a) any series circuit diagram with a component (e.g. lamp) **(1)** and an ammeter **(1)**

(b) stopwatch / timer **(1)**

13 Current, resistance and pd

1 resistance **(1)**

2 The current flowing through a resistor **(1)** at constant temperature is directly proportional to the potential difference across the resistor **(1)**.

3 (a) Potential difference $= I R = 0.20 A \times 60 \Omega$ **(1)** $= 12$ **(1)** V

(b) Current $I = V / R = 22 V / 55 \Omega$ **(1)** $= 0.40$ **(1)** A

4 (a) line A – straight line through origin **(1)**
line B – straight line through origin – different gradient **(1)**

(b) line with smaller gradient **(1)**

14 Required practical – Investigating resistance

1 Ammeter is connected in series but voltmeter is connected in parallel across the component **(1)**.

2 $R = V / I$ so $R = 90 V / 1.5$ **(1)** $A = 60$ **(1)** Ω

3 All circuit symbols correct (2 cells, 2 lamps, 1 ammeter, 1 voltmeter, wire) **(1)**. Ammeter connected in series **(1)**. Voltmeter connected in parallel with one lamp **(1)**.

4 (a) Fixed resistor. **(1)**

(b) Filament lamp. **(1)**

(c) Diode. **(1)**

15 Resistors

1 (a) As the potential difference increases, the current increases **(1)** in a linear / proportional relationship **(1)**.

(b) As the potential difference increases the current increases **(1)** but the gradient of the line gets less steep / shallower, or increase in current becomes smaller as the potential difference continues to increase **(1)**.

2 (a) Fixed resistor: as graph A in Q1 **(1)**

Filament lamp: as graph B in Q1 **(1)**

(b) The different shaped graphs are because the fixed resistor is ohmic / obeys Ohm's law, so the current and potential difference have a proportional relationship **(1)**; the filament lamp does not obey Ohm's law so the relationship between current and potential difference is not proportional / current begins to level off as potential difference increases **(1)**.

3 Data can be collected using an ammeter to measure current **(1)** and a voltmeter to measure potential difference **(1)**. A wire should be included and a fixed resistor **(1)** to prevent overheating. A range of potential difference **(1)** measurements should be made so that resistance can be calculated using the equation $R = V / I$ **(1)**.

16 LDRs and thermistors

1 light **(1)**

2

Light-dependent resistor (LDR)	Thermistor
(1)	**(1)**

3 (a) The resistance goes down as the light becomes more intense (brighter) (more current flows) **(1)**.

(b) The resistance goes down as the temperature goes up (more current flows) **(1)**.

4 The thermistor reacts to rise in temperature **(1)** in the engine. Above a certain temperature, it allows current **(1)** in the circuit to flow to a fan, which cools **(1)** the engine.

17 Required practical – Investigating *I*–*V* characteristics

1 (a) ammeter connected in series **(1)**. voltmeter connected in parallel across the component to be tested **(1)**.

Component being tested

(b) (i) Potential difference (*V*) **(1)**

(ii) Current (*I*) **(1)** (can be in reverse order)

(c) The terminal connections should be reversed to obtain negative values **(1)**.

(d) *y*-axis: current (*I*), *x*- axis: potential difference (*V*) **(1)** (both needed)

2 (i) In an ohmic conductor, the current is directly proportional to potential difference **(1)**.

(ii) The resistance stays constant **(1)**.

3 Resistors can become hot and cause burns or fire **(1)**.

18 Series and parallel circuits

1 (a) In a series circuit the current flowing through each component is the same **(1)**. In a parallel circuit, the current is shared between the components **(1)**.

(b) Series: $A_2 = 3$ A, $A_3 = 3$ A **(1)** (both needed)

Parallel: $A_2 = 1$ A, $A_3 = 1$ A, $A_4 = 1$ A **(1)** (all three needed)

2 (a) In a series circuit, the total potential difference supplied is shared between the components **(1)**. In a parallel circuit, the potential difference across each component is the same as the potential difference supplied **(1)**.

(b) Series: $V_2 = 3$ V, $V_3 = 3$ V, $V_4 = 3$ V **(1)** (all three needed)

Parallel: $V_2 = 9$ V, $V_3 = 9$ V, $V_4 = 9$ V **(1)** (all three needed)

3 The total resistance of two or more resistors arranged in series is equal to **(1)** the sum of the resistance of each component **(1)**. The total resistance of two or more resistors arranged in parallel is less than **(1)** the resistance of the smallest individual resistor **(1)**.

19 ac and dc

1 (a) Direct potential difference is constant **(1)** and the current flows in the same direction **(1)**.

(b) Alternating potential difference is changeable **(1)** and the current constantly changes direction **(1)**.

2 230 V and 50 Hz **(1)**

3 (a) The current is a direct current **(1)** because the electrons all flow in the same direction **(1)**.

(b) There should be one horizontal line anywhere on the screen **(1)**.

20 Mains electricity

1 (a) earth wire (green and yellow) **(1)**, live wire (brown) **(1)**, neutral wire (blue) **(1)**, fuse **(1)**

(b) live wire **(1)** because it carries the current into the appliance **(1)**

2 (a) alternating current **(1)**

(b) about 230 V **(1)**

(c) The earth wire is at 0 V **(1)** and only carries a current if there is a fault **(1)**.

(d) 50 Hz **(1)**

3 When a large current enters the live wire **(1)**, this produces thermal energy **(1)**, which melts the wire in the fuse **(1)** and the circuit is then broken **(1)**.

4 The earth wire is connected to the metal casing **(1)**. If the live wire becomes loose and touches anything metallic, the user is protected because the current passes out through the earth wire **(1)** rather than through the user **(1)**.

21 Electrical power

1 $P = I V = 5$ A $\times 230$ V **(1)**

Power $= 1150$ **(1)** W

2 (a) $P = I V$ so $I = P / V$ **(1)** $= 3$ W $/ 6$ V **(1)**

Current $= 0.5$ **(1)** A

(b) $P = I^2 R$ **(1)** $= (0.5$ A$)^2 \times 240\ \Omega$ **(1)**

Power $= 60$ **(1)** W

3 Power $= 6 \times 230$ (W) **(1)**

4 (a) $I = V / R = 80$ V $/ 8\ \Omega$ **(1)** $= 10$ **(1)** A

(b) Power $P = I V$ so $P = 10$ A $\times 80$ V **(1)** $= 800$ **(1)** W

or $P = I^2 R$ so $P = 100$ A $\times 8\ \Omega$ **(1)** $= 800$ **(1)** W

22 Electrical energy

1 force **(1)**

2 $E = Q V = 30$ C $\times 9$ V **(1)** $= 270$ **(1)** J

3 (a) $Q = I t = 0.2$ A $\times 4$ V **(1)** $= 0.8$ **(1)** C

(b) $E = Q V = 0.8$ C $\times 30$ s **(1)** $= 24$ **(1)** joules / J **(1)**

4 (a) The power of a circuit device is a measure of the rate of energy transfer / how fast the energy is transferred by the device **(1)**.

(b) Energy transferred is the amount of power over a given time **(1)** and the power of a device is the product of the current passing through it and the potential difference across it **(1)**.

23 The National Grid

1 (a) When a current flows through a wire, the resistance of a wire **(1)** causes energy to be transferred to the wire and heating it **(1)**.

(b) As the voltage is increased so the current goes down **(1)**, so this reduces the heating effect due to resistance **(1)** and means that less energy is wasted in transmission **(1)**.

(c) Wasting less energy in transmission means that more energy is transferred to where it is needed **(1)**, making the National Grid an efficient way to transmit energy **(1)**.

(d) The voltages are high enough to kill you if you touch or come into contact with a transmission line **(1)**.

2 Any two from: step-up transformers increase voltage and so lower the current, reducing the heating losses **(1)**; wires are thermally insulated **(1)**; wires of low resistance are used **(1)**.

3 Step-up transformers are used to increase the voltage **(1)** as it leaves the power station for transmission through the National Grid **(1)**. Near homes, step-down transformers are used to reduce the voltage **(1)** to make it safer for use in houses **(1)**.

24 Static electricity

1 electrons on insulators **(1)**

2 (a) Friction transfers electrons to another material **(1)**.

(b) Friction transfers electrons from another material **(1)**.

3 The student causes a charge on the balloon by transferring electrons from the jumper to the balloon **(1)**. The negative charges on the balloon repel the electrons in the wall **(1)**, inducing a positive charge on the wall **(1)** which attracts the negatively charged balloon **(1)**.

4 Insulators do not allow electrons to flow **(1)**. Instead the electrons either collect on the insulator (building up a charge) **(1)** or are knocked off (leaving a positive charge) **(1)**. Conductors allow electrons to flow **(1)**. Mutually repelling electrons will then flow away and this dissipates any charge build-up **(1)**.

25 Electric fields

1 alpha particle (1) and proton (1)

2 An electric field is a region in space (1) where a charged particle may experience a force (1).

3 (a) high density lines of flux (1), radial field (1), arrows pointing outwards (1)

radial field

(b) The alpha particle will move away from the charge (1) because like charges repel. (1)

4 The strength of an electric field of a charged object decreases (1) with increasing distance from the charged object. (1)

26 Extended response – Electricity

The answer should include some of the following points: (6)

- The thermistor can be connected in series with an ammeter to measure current with a voltmeter connected in parallel across it to measure potential difference.
- Ohm's law can be referred to in calculating the resistance.
- When the temperature is low the resistance of the thermistor will be high, allowing only a small current to flow.
- When the temperature is high the resistance of the thermistor will be low, allowing a larger current to flow.
- The light-dependent resistor can be connected in series with an ammeter to measure current with a voltmeter connected in parallel across it to measure potential difference.
- When light levels are low (dark) the resistance of the light-dependent resistor will be high, allowing only a small current to flow.
- When light levels are high (bright) the resistance of the light-dependent resistor will be low, allowing a larger current to flow.
- Thermistors can be used in fire alarms as a temperature sensor to switch on an alarm.
- Light-dependent resistors can be used in security systems as a light sensor to switch on a light.

27 Density

1 (a) 1. solid

2. liquid

3. gas (1)

(b) In a solid, mass per unit volume is higher than for a liquid or a gas because the particles are very close together (1). In a liquid, mass per unit volume is lower than that for a solid, because the particles are further apart, but higher than that for a gas because the particles are closer together (1). In a gas, mass per unit volume is low because the particles are furthest apart (1).

2 Density is calculated by dividing its mass by its volume (1).

3 (a) Density = m/V = 1650 kg / 3 m^3 (1) = 550 (1) kg/m^3

(b) Density = m/V = 4000 kg / 5 m^3 (1) = 800 (1) kg/m^3

28 Required practical – Investigating density

1 (a) mass (1)

(b) electronic balance (1)

2 (a) For regularly shaped solids: any one of the following methods:

1. Volume can be directly measured using Vernier callipers / ruler to measure the length, width and height of the object (1). The measurements are then multiplied together to find the volume, e.g. 3 cm × 3 cm × 3 cm to give the volume of a 3-cm cube (1).

2. If the object is a regular shape, e.g. cube, cylinder, sphere, prism, the appropriate mathematical expression can be used (1), e.g. use 4 / 3 π r^3 to find the volume of a sphere (1).

3. If the density and mass are already known the volume can be calculated by using the equation (1), i.e. volume = mass / density (1).

(b) For an irregular solid: any one of the following methods:

1. Pour water into a measuring cylinder to a specific level and record the level (1). Add the object to the water and record the new water level. The difference between the new water level and the original level will be the object's volume (1).

2. Use a Eureka can by filling it with water until the water runs out from the spout (1). When no more water runs out, carefully place the irregular solid into the can and measure the volume of water displaced through the spout by collecting the water in a measuring cylinder (1).

3 (a) Place a measuring cylinder on a balance and then zero the scales with no liquid in the measuring cylinder (1). Add the liquid and measure the level (1). Record the mass of the liquid (in g) from the balance and the volume (in cm^3) by reading from the level in the measuring cylinder (1).

(b) Take the value at the bottom of the meniscus (1) making sure that the reading is made at 'eye level', to avoid a 'parallax error' (1).

(c) Density = mass / volume so ρ = 121 g / 205 cm^3 (1) = 0.59 (1) g/cm^3

29 Changes of state

1 In a liquid there are some intermolecular forces between particles as they move round each other (1). In a gas there are almost no intermolecular forces as the particles are far apart (1).

2 physical change (1)

3 melts; boils; evaporates; condenses; freezes; 1 or 2 correct: **1 mark**; 3 or 4 correct: **2 marks**; all 5 correct: **3 marks**

4 Energy is transferred to the ice → energy is transferred to surroundings. (1)

5 At boiling point the liquid changes state (1) so the energy applied after boiling point is reached goes into breaking bonds (1) between the liquid particles. The particles gain more energy and become a gas (1).

30 Internal energy

1 the total sum of the kinetic and potential energies of the particles inside the system (1)

2 At boiling point / latent heat of vaporisation there will be a change / increase to the potential energy of the particles (1) but the kinetic energy of the particles will not change (1).

3 (a) When temperature rises due to heating, internal energy increases (1) because the kinetic energy of the particles increases (1).

(b) When temperature does not rise, due to heating, internal energy increases (1) because the potential energy of the particles increases (1).

4 When the water vapour condenses into a liquid there will be no change in the kinetic energy (1) of the water particles so the temperature does not change (1) but there will be a change in the potential energy (1) of the water particles as they move from a gas state to a liquid state.

31 Specific latent heat

1 Specific latent heat is the energy that must be transferred to change 1 kg of a material from one state of matter to another (1).

2 temperature of the mass (1)

3 $E = m L$ = 25 kg × 336 000 J/kg (1) = 8400 000 (1) J

4 (a) Melting – B (1)

(b) Boiling – D (1)

(c) Specific latent heat of fusion – B (1)

(d) Specific latent heat of vaporisation – D (1)

(e) The energy being transferred to the material is breaking bonds (1); as a result, the material undergoes a phase change (1).

5 $E = m L$ = 36 kg × 2260 kJ/kg (1) = 81 360 (1) kJ

32 Particle motion in gases

1 Temperature is a measurement of the average kinetic energy of the particles in a material (1).

2 At a constant volume, the pressure and temperature of a gas are directly proportional (1).

3 (a) As the temperature increases the particles will move faster (1) because they gain more energy (1).

(b) As the particles are moving faster they will collide with the container walls more often (1), therefore increasing the pressure (1).

(c) It increases (1).

33 Pressure in gases

1 When particles of a gas collide (1) with a surface they exert a force at right angles to the surface (1) resulting in pressure (1).

2 Volume is inversely proportional to pressure **(1)**.

3 (a) When the volume of a gas, at constant temperature, is increased, the particles collide with the walls of the container / surface less often **(1)** so the force they exert is less / lower **(1)** so the pressure / force per unit area is less / lower **(1)**.

    (b) When the volume of a gas, at constant temperature, is decreased, the particles collide with the walls of the container / surface more often **(1)** so the force they exert is more / higher **(1)** so the pressure / force per unit area is more / higher **(1)**.

4 $P_1 V_1 = P_2 V_2$ so 100 kPa × 230 cm³ = 280 kPa × V_2 **(1)**. V_2 = 100 kPa × 230 cm³ / 280 kPa **(1)** = 82.1 **(1)** cm³

34 Extended response – Particle model

The answer should include some of the following points: **(6)**

- Solid, liquid and gas states of matter have increasing kinetic energy of particles.
- Thermal energy input or output will result in changes to the thermal energy store of the system and will result in changes of state or a change in temperature.
- Changes in states of matter are reversible because the material recovers its original properties if the change is reversed.
- Thermal energy input does not always result in a temperature rise if the energy is used to make or break bonds between particles / result in a change of state.
- Latent heat is the amount of heat / thermal energy required by a substance to undergo a change of state.
- The thermal energy required to change from solid / ice to water (accept converse) is called the latent heat of fusion and is calculated using $E = m L$.
- The thermal energy required to change from liquid to gas / water to steam (accept converse) is called the latent heat of vaporisation and is calculated using $E = m L$.

35 The structure of the atom

1 (a) Protons – labelled in the nucleus (+ charge) **(1)**

    (b) Neutrons – labelled in nucleus (0 charge) **(1)**

    (c) Electrons – labelled as orbiting (- charge) **(1)**

2 (a) The number of positively charged protons **(1)** in the nucleus is equal to the number of negatively charged electrons **(1)** orbiting the nucleus.

    (b) The atom will become a positively charged ion / charge of +1 **(1)**.

3 Size of an atom: 10^{-10} m **(1)**

    Size of a nucleus: 10^{-15} m **(1)**

4 When an electron absorbs electromagnetic radiation **(1)** it will move to a higher energy level **(1)**. When the electron moves back from a higher energy level to a lower energy level **(1)** it will emit electromagnetic radiation **(1)**.

36 Atoms, isotopes and ions

1 (a) the name given to particles in the nucleus **(1)**

    (b) the number of protons in the nucleus **(1)**

    (c) the total number of protons and neutrons in the nucleus **(1)**

2 The number of neutrons is different **(1)**.

3 Isotopes will be neutral because the number of positively charged protons **(1)** still equals the number of negatively charged electrons **(1)**.

4 atoms: Cu, B; ions: F–, Na+, K+ (4 or 5 correct, **2 marks**; 2 or 3 correct, **1 mark**, 1 correct, **0 marks**)

5 Any two of the following explanations:

    1) An atom can lose one or more electrons by friction **(1)** where contact forces rub electrons away **(1)** from the atom.

    2) An atom can lose one or more electrons by ionising radiation **(1)**, where electrons are removed from the atom by an alpha or beta particle colliding **(1)** with an electron.

    3) An atom or molecule can lose one or more electrons by electrolysis **(1)** when it was previously bonded in an ionic compound and is separated in solution in an electrolytic cell **(1)**.

37 Models of the atom

1 the electron **(1)**

2 The plum pudding model showed the atom as a 'solid', positively charged **(1)** particle containing a distribution of negatively charged electrons **(1)** whereas the nuclear model showed the atom as having a tiny, dense, positively charged nucleus **(1)** surrounded by orbiting negatively charged electrons **(1)**.

3 Rutherford fired positively charged alpha particles at atoms of gold foil and most went through, showing that most of the atom was space / a void **(1)**. Some were repelled or deflected **(1)**, showing that the nucleus was positively charged **(1)**.

4 (a) The particle Chadwick had found was electrically neutral **(1)** and so could not be a proton / must be a new particle **(1)**.

    (b) neutron **(1)**

38 Radioactive decay

1 (a) Activity is the rate **(1)** at which the unstable / radioactive nuclei decay per second **(1)**.

    (b) The unit of activity is the becquerel (Bq) **(1)**.

    (c) Count rate is the number of counts of radioactive decay **(1)** per unit of time / second / minute **(1)**.

2 The number of neutrons decreases by 1 **(1)**.

3 electromagnetic radiation **(1)**

4 (a) Alpha radiation / particle: **(1)** the alpha particle consists of 4 nucleons / 2 protons and 2 neutrons / a 'helium' nucleus **(1)**

    (b) Beta radiation / particle: **(1)** a neutron changes to a proton increasing the positive charge by 1 **(1)**

39 Nuclear radiation

1 helium nucleus with charge +2 **(1)**

2 alpha – very low, stopped by 10 cm of air

beta minus – low, stopped by thin aluminium

gamma – very high, stopped by very thick lead

all correct **(2)**, 2 correct **(1)**

3 (a) no change in relative atomic mass **(1)**

    (b) high-energy electron emitted from the nucleus **(1)**

    (c) moderately ionising **(1)**

4 Compared with other types of ionising radiation, the chance of collision with air particles at close range is high **(1)** because the alpha particles have a large positive charge / are massive compared with other types of radiation **(1)**. Once an alpha particle has collided with another particle it loses its energy **(1)**.

40 Uses of nuclear radiation

1 (a) Beta **(1)** radiation is used because alpha radiation / particles would not pass through **(1)** and gamma radiation / waves / rays would pass too easily **(1)**.

    (b) (i) The paper has become too thick **(1)**.

       (ii) The pressure on the rollers would be increased to make the paper thinner **(1)**.

2 They have high frequency / they carry large amounts of energy **(1)**.

3 (a) Alpha particles cannot pass through to the outside of the smoke alarm **(1)** and they are contained in a metal box / stopped by about 10 cm of air / are situated away from normal traffic of people **(1)**.

    (b) The smoke particles absorb the alpha particles **(1)** so the current falls / is broken and this triggers the bell to ring **(1)**.

4 Beta particles are less ionising than alpha particles **(1)** so they are much less likely to cause damage to body cells **(1)**.

41 Nuclear equations

1 (a) α **(1)**

    (b) β **(1)**

2 The mass number is reduced by 4 **(1)**.

3 (a) (for nitrogen) 7 **(1)**

    (b) (for phosphorus) 15 **(1)**

4 (a) beta-plus (positron) **(1)**

    (b) alpha particle **(1)**

    (c) neutron **(1)**

5 (a) add 208 to Po **(1)**; type of decay = alpha **(1)**

    (b) add 86 to Rn **(1)**; type of decay = alpha **(1)**

    (c) add 42 to Ca **(1)**; type of decay = beta-minus **(1)**

    (d) add 9 to Be **(1)**; type of decay = neutron **(1)**

42 Half-life

1 random **(1)**

2 Half-life is the time taken for half the nuclei in a radioactive isotope to decay **(1)**.

3 (a) 8 million nuclei **(1)**

    (b) 9.3 minutes = 3 half-lives **(1)** so, after 1 half-life, 8 million nuclei left, after 2 half-lives, 4 million nuclei left, and, after 3 half-lives, 2 million nuclei left **(1)**

4 activity = 400 Bq at 1.5 minutes **(1)** (between 1.3 and 1.7 is allowed). Half this activity = 200 Bq, at 6.5 **(1)** minutes (between 6.3 and 6.7 is allowed), so the half-life is 6.5 min – 1.5 min = 5 min **(1)**. (Answers between 4.7 and 5.3 min are allowed.) *(If you used other points on your graph and got an answer of around 5 min you would get full marks. For this question your working can just be pairs of lines drawn on the graph.)*

43 Contamination and irradiation

1 irradiation **(1)**

2 (a) External contamination: radioactive particles come into contact with skin, hair or clothing **(1)**.

   (b) Internal contamination: a radioactive source is eaten, drunk or inhaled **(1)**.

   (c) Irradiation: a person becomes exposed to an external source of ionising radiation **(1)**.

3 (a) Any suitable example, e.g. contaminated soil may get on to hands **(1)**.

   (b) Any suitable example, e.g. contaminated dust or radon gas may be inhaled **(1)**.

4 Internal contamination means that the alpha particles come into contact with the body through inhalation or ingestion **(1)**, where they are likely to cause internal tissue damage **(1)**. Alpha particles that are irradiated are less likely to cause damage because they have to travel through air **(1)** and are therefore less likely to ionise body cells **(1)** (at distances of over 10 cm).

44 Hazards of radiation

1 alpha particles **(1)**

2 1. Limit the time of exposure / keep the time that a person needs to be in contact with the ionising source as low as possible **(1)**.

   2. Wear protective clothing / wearing a lead apron will absorb much of the ionising radiation **(1)**.

   3. Increase the distance from the radioactive source / the further a person is from the ionising radiation, the less damage it will do **(1)**.

3 A source of alpha particles with high activity inside the body will ionise body cells **(1)** because they are highly ionising / massive / undergo many collisions **(1)** before transferring all of their ionising energy **(1)**. Gamma-rays can pass out of the body fairly easily **(1)** without causing much damage to cells **(1)**.

4 Radioactive tongs allow the source to be kept as far as possible away from a person's hand **(1)** and allow it to be pointed away from people at all times **(1)**.

5 Those who use X-rays on a regular basis, such as medical workers, would have a high exposure / dose of radiation, which would cause damage if the dose was too high **(1)**. They leave the room so that they are not exposed to high levels of cumulative radiation / high dose **(1)**. The number of X-rays that a patient has is carefully monitored to minimise risk of high dose / exposure to high levels of radiation **(1)**.

45 Background radiation

1 about 14% **(1)**

2 Levels can vary because of the different rocks **(1)** that occur naturally in the environment. They can also vary due to the use of different rocks such as granite **(1)** in buildings.

3 Natural: air **(1)** and **two** of the following – cosmic rays, rocks in the ground, food **(1)**

   Manufactured: nuclear power, medical treatment, nuclear weapons **(1)** (all three needed for mark)

4 (a) (add the three values and divide by 3) SE 0.27 Bq, SW 0.30 Bq **(1)** (both needed for mark)

   (b) The South West (has the highest average level of background radiation) **(1)**.

46 Medical uses

1 Gamma radiation penetrates deeper from outside the body than alpha or beta radiation **(1)**.

2 Several beams of gamma-rays are fired, from different positions, towards the centre of the cancer tumour **(1)**. Using a number of beams means that more energy **(1)** can be focused in one place. The cancer tumour receives most of the energy and the surrounding healthy tissue receives less **(1)**.

3 A medical tracer is a radioactive solution that contains a gamma-emitting radioisotope **(1)**. It is injected into the patient and is then absorbed by the organ being examined **(1)**. A special camera detects the gamma radiation emitted by the solution **(1)**. The detected waves are used to build up an image of where the radioisotope is located in the organ **(1)**.

4 The radioactive isotope must have a half-life long enough to give a useful image **(1)**, but short enough so that its nuclei have mostly decayed after the image has been taken **(1)**.

47 Nuclear fission

1 Left nucleus: uranium-235 **(1)**. Two new nuclei: daughter nuclei **(1)**. Small single particles – neutrons **(1)**.

2 (a) Nuclear fission is the splitting **(1)** of a large and unstable nucleus (e.g. uranium or plutonium) **(1)**.

   (b) Usually, for fission to occur the unstable nucleus **(1)** must first absorb a neutron **(1)**.

3 (a) A chain reaction occurs as neutrons are released from a fission reaction and are absorbed by more uranium nuclei that also undergo fission **(1)**. As more than one neutron is released per fission reaction **(1)** this leads to more and more fission reactions occurring which could lead to an explosion **(1)**.

   (b) Control rods are used to absorb excess neutrons **(1)** to keep the chain reaction at a steady rate **(1)**.

   (c)

Uranium atom absorbing / about to absorb a neutron **(1)**. Three neutrons and energy released **(1)**. At least two more uranium atoms shown **(1)** each releasing three neutrons **(1)**.

   (d) Controlled chain reactions are used in nuclear power stations **(1)**.

48 Nuclear fusion

1 hydrogen nuclei → helium nuclei **(1)**

2 Fusion needs high pressures and temperatures **(1)**. At present, this requires more energy than is released by fusion **(1)**.

3 (a) the Sun **(1)**

   (b) energy as heat / light **(1)**

   (c) stars **(1)**

4 (a) Nuclei need to get very close to each other before fusion can happen **(1)**. Electrostatic repulsion means that the positive charges of the nuclei repel each other **(1)**.

   (b) To give the nuclei enough energy **(1)** to overcome this, very high temperatures **(1)** and pressures **(1)** are needed.

49 Extended response – Radioactivity

The answer should include some of the following points: **(6)**

- All three types of radiation can pass into / penetrate different materials.
- Alpha particles have high relative mass and so transfer a lot of energy when they collide, so they are good at ionising.
- Alpha particles produce a lot of ions in a short distance, losing energy each time.
- Alpha particles have a short penetration distance so are absorbed by low density / thin materials such as a few centimetres of air and a sheet of paper.
- Beta particles have a low relative mass and can pass into / through more materials than alpha particles.
- Beta particles are less ionising than alpha particles and can be absorbed by 3-mm-thick aluminium.
- Gamma-rays are high-frequency EM waves and can travel a few kilometres in air.
- Gamma-rays are weakly ionising and need thick lead or several metres of concrete to absorb them.

50 Scalars and vectors

1 (a) Scalars: speed, energy, temperature, mass, distance **(1)**

   Vectors: acceleration, displacement, force, velocity, momentum **(1)**

   (b) Any correct choice and explanation, e.g. mass **(1)** is a scalar because it has a size / magnitude **(1)** but no direction **(1)**.

2 (a) weight **(1)**

   (b) Weight has size / magnitude and direction but the other quantities just have a magnitude **(1)**.

3 (a) (i) Velocity is used because both a size and a direction are given **(1)**.

      (ii) The students are jogging in opposite directions so the negative sign for one student indicates this **(1)**.

(b) The length of the arrow is proportional to the magnitude of the vector (in this case velocity) **(1)**. An increase in velocity to 3 m/s would mean an arrow 1½ times longer than that for 2 m/s **(1)**.

51 Interacting forces

1 gravitational **(1)**, magnetic **(1)**, electrostatic **(1)**

2 Like poles and charges repel **(1)**.

3 Weight and normal contact force are both vectors because they have a direction **(1)**. Weight is measured downwards **(1)** whereas normal contact force is measured upwards/opposite to weight **(1)**.

4 (a) pull (by the student on the bag) and friction/drag of the bag against the floor **(1)**

(b) weight and normal contact/reaction force **(1)**

5 As the skydiver leaves the plane, weight acting downwards is greater than air resistance acting upwards so he accelerates **(1)**. As speed increases, air resistance increases to become equal to weight, so there is no net force / terminal velocity reached **(1)**. When the skydiver opens the parachute, air resistance upwards is greater than weight downwards so he decelerates **(1)**. The skydiver decelerates until air resistance upwards equals weight downwards – there is no net force (so a new terminal velocity is reached) **(1)**. (or similar wording)

52 Gravity, weight and mass

1 (a) The mass of the LRV on the Moon is 210 kg **(1)** because the mass of an object does not change if nothing is added or removed **(1)**.

(b)

Arrow points vertically downwards / top of arrow estimated around the seat area of the LVR **(1)**. (both points needed for mark) The centre of mass is where the weight of a body can be assumed to act downwards through a single point **(1)**.

2 $W = m\,g$ so $(1 + 2 + 1.5)$ kg $\times$ 10 N/kg **(1)** = 4.5 kg $\times$ 10 N/kg = 45 **(1)** N

3 calculating correct masses for all three items **(1)**

selecting correct items **(1)** (clothes 10.5 kg + camera bag 5.5 kg + jacket 3.5 kg) = 19.5 kg **(1)**

53 Resultant forces

1 Resultant force is the net force after adding together all the forces acting on an object / is the single force that has the same effect on an object as all the forces acting on it **(1)**.

2 (a) A: 9.5 N; **(1)** B: 2 N; **(1)** C: 4.5 N; **(1)** D: 12.75 N **(1)**

(b) A: up; **(1)** B: up; **(1)** C: to the right; **(1)** D: to the left **(1)**

3 4 N **(1)**

4 (a) resultant force = positive direction – negative direction = 30 N – 10 N – 1 N **(1)** = 19 N **(1)**

(b) The resultant force is zero / 0 N **(1)** so the velocity is constant / stays the same **(1)**.

54 Work and energy

1 gravitational potential energy **(1)**

2 (a) Work done against friction will lead to a rise in the thermal energy store of the object **(1)**, this energy is then dissipated to the environment **(1)**.

(b) The greater the amount of friction, the more work that has to be done **(1)** to move the body through the same distance **(1)**.

3 $W = F\,s = 80$ N $\times$ 60 m **(1)** = 4800 **(1)** J

4 (a) $h = E_p / (m\,g)$ so $h = 320 / (8 \times 10)$ **(1)** (remember to convert the grams to kilograms) = 4 **(1)** m

(b) Use $W = F\,s$ so $F = W / s$ **(1)** and $F = 320 / 4$ **(1)** = 80 **(1)** N

55 Forces and elasticity

1 friction **(1)**

2 (a) Tension: washing line (or any valid example) **(1)**

(b) Compression: G-clamp, pliers (or any valid example) **(1)**

(c) Elastic distortion: fishing rod (with a fish on the line) (or any valid example) **(1)**

(d) Inelastic distortion: dented can or deformed spring (or any valid example) **(1)**

3 After testing, Beam 1 would return to the same size and shape as before the test **(1)** and would be intact **(1)**. Beam 2 would distort and change shape **(1)** but would (probably) still be intact **(1)**.

56 Force and extension

1 Elastic deformation means that the object will change shape in direct proportion to the force(s) exerted, up to the limit of proportionality **(1)**, and the change in shape is not permanent **(1)**. Inelastic deformation means that the object will change shape beyond the limit of proportionality / the limit of proportionality is exceeded **(1)** and the change in shape will be permanent **(1)**.

2 20 N **(1)**

3 Extension = 0.07 m – 0.03 m = 0.04 m

Force = (spring constant / k) $\times$ extension = 80 N $\times$ 0.04 m **(1)**

Force = 3.2 **(1)** N **(1)**

4 (a) $F = k\,e$ so $k = F / e$ **(1)** = 30 N / 0.15 m **(1)** = 200 **(1)** N/m

(b) $E_e = \frac{1}{2}\,k\,e^2 = \frac{1}{2} \times 200$ N/m $\times (0.15$ m$)^2$ **(1)** = 2.25 **(1)** J

57 Required practical – Force and extension

1 (a) Hang a spring from a clamp attached to a retort stand and measure the length before any masses or weights are added using a half-metre ruler, marked in mm **(1)**. Carefully add the first mass or weight and measure the total length of the extended spring **(1)**. Unload the mass or weight and re-measure the spring to make sure that

the original length has not changed **(1)**. Add at least five masses or weights and repeat the measurements each time **(1)**.

(b) To check that the elastic potential energy can all be recovered **(1)** and is not transferred to cause a permanent change of shape in the spring **(1)**.

(c) Masses must be converted to force (N) by using $W = m \times g$ / $F = m \times g$ **(1)**. The extension of the spring must be calculated for each force by taking away the original length of the spring from each reading **(1)**. Extension measurements should be converted to metres **(1)**.

(d) (i) The area under the graph equals the work done / the energy stored in the spring as elastic potential energy **(1)**.

(ii) The gradient of the linear part of the force–extension graph gives the spring constant k **(1)**.

(e) limit of proportionality **(1)**

(f) elastic potential energy = 0.5 $\times$ spring constant $\times$ extension^2 or $E_e = \frac{1}{2}\,k\,e^2$ **(1)**

2 The length of a spring is measured with no force applied to the spring whereas the extension of a spring is the length of the spring measured under load / force less the original length **(1)**.

58 Moments

1 a perpendicular force acting at a distance from a pivot **(1)**

2 When an object is balanced the clockwise moment **(1)** is equal to the anticlockwise moment **(1)**.

3 $M = F\,d = 25$ N $\times$ 0.28 m **(1)** = 7 **(1)** N m **(1)**

4 (a) not in equilibrium **(1)**

moment for B = 300 N $\times$ 0.8 m = 240 N m **(1)**

moment for A = 250 N $\times$ 1.2 m = 300 N m **(1)**

(b) Moment for B must change to equal 300 N m **(1)** so distance must change to 300 N m / 300 N = 1 m **(1)**.

59 Levers and gears

1 Levers and gears transmit the rotational effects of forces **(1)**.

2 (a) (i) input forces as shown **(1)** (both needed)

(ii) output forces as shown **(1)** (both needed)

(iii) pivots as shown **(1)** (both needed)

(b) The input force is the force provided by the user of the lever **(1)**. The output force is the force that results from the input force **(1)**.

3 For a high gear, the driver gear has a greater diameter than the driven gear **(1)** and the output is low for a given input force **(1)**. For a low gear, the driver gear has a similar diameter to the driven gear **(1)** and the output is high for a given input force **(1)**.

60 Pressure

1 Pressure in fluids causes a force to act at right angles to the surface **(1)**.

2 $P = F / A$ so $P = 25 / 0.0625$ **(1)** $= 400$ **(1)** Pa

3 The weight of the box is found by $F = P A$ so $F = 2000$ Pa $\times 0.25$ m² **(1)** $= 500$ **(1)** N

4 (a) Atmospheric pressure describes a column of air reaching from the Earth's surface to the top of the atmosphere **(1)**, and covering one square metre of the Earth **(1)** containing a mass of air equal to 10 000 kg **(1)**.

   (b) $p = F / A$ so $F = p A = 100 000$ Pa $\times 5 000$ m² **(1)** $= 5 \times 10^8$ **(1)** N

61 Distance and displacement

1 A to C $= 75$ m **(1)**

2 Distance does not involve a direction and so is a scalar quantity **(1)**. Displacement involves both the distance an object moves and the direction that it has moved in from its starting point so it is a vector quantity **(1)**.

3 (a) The circumference of the Ferris wheel is $2 \pi \times (15 / 2) = 47.1$ m **(1)**. The wheel completed three cycles so the total distance travelled was 3×47.1 **(1)** $= 141.3$ m **(1)**. (accept 141 m)

   (b) The final displacement was 0 m **(1)** as the girls returned to the starting point at the end of the ride **(1)**.

62 Speed and velocity

1 Average speed $= 10 000$ m $/ 2400$ s **(1)** $= 4.17$ **(1)** m/s

2 (a) Any **three** of the following: age, terrain, fitness, distance travelled **(1)**

   (b) (i) walking: 1.5 m/s **(1)**

      (ii) running: 3 m/s **(1)**

      (iii) cycling: 6 m/s **(1)**

3 The speed of the satellite is constant because the distance being covered each second is constant **(1)**, but the velocity changes constantly because the direction of motion is constantly changing **(1)**.

4 (a) $s = v t$, so distance $= 4 \times (15 \times 60)$ **(1)** $= 3600$ **(1)** m

   (b) The term velocity is used because the boat has both a speed **(1)** and a direction **(1)**.

   (c) At the finish of the journey by boat, the displacement of the team from the boathouse is 3600 m **(1)**. As they return to the boathouse by bus, the displacement decreases **(1)** until they arrive back at the boathouse where the final displacement is 0 m **(1)**.

63 Distance–time graphs

1 (a) (i) B **(1)**

      (ii) C **(1)**

   (b) Evidence of attempt to calculate the gradient of the slope to find speed / use of change in distance divided by the change in time / speed = distance / time, **(1)** so $s = 20 / 40$ **(1)** $= 0.5$ **(1)** m/s.

   (c) walking (slowly) **(1)** as the average walking speed is 1.5 m/s **(1)**

   (d) In part A, the runner travels 60 m in 40 s. Speed = distance / time **(1)** = 60 m / 40 s **(1)** = 1.5 **(1)** m/s. (You can use any part A of the graph to read off the distance and the time as the line is straight; you should always get the same speed.)

   (e) Displacement is the length and direction of a straight line between the runner's home and the park **(1)**, but the distance the runner ran may have included bends and corners on the path that the runner took **(1)**.

64 Velocity–time graphs

1 (a) $a = \Delta v / t = 4 / 5$ **(1)** $= 0.8$ **(1)** m/s² **(1)**

2 (a) The velocity of the car is increasing steadily **(1)**.

   (b) A right-angled triangle with a horizontal side and a vertical side that covers as much of the line as possible for precision **(1)**.

   (c) Change in velocity $= 30 - 0$ m/s. Time taken for change $= 5 - 0$ s. Acceleration $= \dfrac{\text{change in velocity}}{\text{time taken}}$ or $a = \Delta v / t = 30$ m/s / 5 s **(1)** $= 6$ **(1)** m/s². (The triangle drawn may be different but the answer should be the same.)

65 Equations of motion

1 4 m/s² **(1)**

2 (a) $a = \Delta v / t$ **(1)** $= (25$ m/s $- 15$ m/s$) / 8$ s **(1)** $= 1.25$ **(1)** m/s²

   (b) $v^2 = u^2 + 2as = (25$ m/s$)^2 + 2(1.25$ m/s² $\times 300$ m$)$ **(1)** $= 1375$ m/s² **(1)**

      $v = \sqrt{1375}$ m/s $= 37$ **(1)** m/s (allow rounding error – answers between 37.00 m/s and 37.10 m/s)

   (c) $v^2 - u^2 = 2 a s$, so $s = (v^2 - u^2) / (2 a)$ **(1)** $= ((5$ m/s$)^2 - 1375$ m/s²$) / (2 \times -2$ m/s²$) =$ **(1)** $= -1350$ m/s² $/ -4$ m/s²

      Distance $= 337.5$ m **(1)**

66 Terminal velocity

1 gravity **(1)**

2 (a) The force of gravity pulls the skydiver downwards **(1)**. Air resistance is small so the resultant force is large **(1)**.

   (b) The skydiver stops accelerating because the air resistance becomes equal to her weight **(1)** so the resultant force is zero **(1)**.

   (c) terminal velocity **(1)**

   (d) The larger surface area increases air resistance **(1)** so the resultant force acts upwards **(1)** slowing the skydiver down **(1)**.

3 Ben should measure and mark the column with equal distances (e.g. every 20 cm) **(1)**. The ball should then be dropped through the viscous liquid and the time recorded between each marker **(1)**. When the ball passes through two marked distances at the same speed, terminal velocity is reached **(1)**. Ben can then use $s = d / t$ to calculate the speed at which terminal velocity occurs **(1)**.

67 Newton's first law

1 (a) The forces on the plane are balanced and there is no net force in any direction **(1)**. Newton's first law says that when there is no net force on an object and it is stationary, it will remain stationary **(1)**.

   (b) The forces on the plane are balanced and there is no net force in any direction **(1)**. Newton's first law says that when there is no net force on an object and it is moving at a constant speed, it will continue to move at a constant speed **(1)**.

2 (a) Resultant force $= 30$ N $+ (-5$ N$) + (-1$ N$)$ **(1)** $= 24$ **(1)** N

   (b) The resultant force is zero / 0 N **(1)** so the velocity is constant / stays the same **(1)**.

3 (a) Assume downwards is positive, so resultant downward force is positive $= 1700$ N $- 1900$ N **(1)** $= -200$ **(1)** N. (You should state which direction you are using as the positive direction.)

   (b) The velocity of the probe towards the Moon will decrease **(1)** because the force produces an upward acceleration / negative acceleration **(1)**.

68 Newton's second law

1 (a) The trolley will accelerate **(1)** in the direction of the pull / force **(1)**.

   (b) The acceleration is smaller / lower **(1)** because the mass is larger **(1)**.

2 (a) $F = m a = 3000$ kg $\times -3$ m/s² **(1)** $= -9000$ **(1)** N

   (b) backwards / in the opposite direction to the motion of the minibus **(1)**

3 (a) $a = F / m = 10 500$ N $/ 640$ kg **(1)** $= 16.4$ **(1)** m/s² **(1)**

   (b) The mass of the car decreases **(1)** so the acceleration will increase **(1)**.

69 Required practical – Force, mass and acceleration

1 Electronic equipment is much more accurate **(1)** than using a ruler and a manual stopwatch to obtain values for distance and time to calculate velocity and acceleration. **(1)** (Reference should be made to distance, time and velocity.)

2 Acceleration is inversely proportional to mass **(1)**.

3 Acceleration is calculated by the change in speed ÷ time taken so two velocity values are needed **(1)**; the time difference between these readings **(1)** is used to obtain a value for the acceleration of the trolley.

4 (a) For a constant slope, as the mass increases, the acceleration will decrease **(1)** due to greater inertial mass **(1)**.

   (b) Newton's second law, $a = F / m$ **(1)**

5. An accelerating mass of greater than a few hundred grams can be dangerous and may hurt somebody if it hits them at speed **(1)**. Any two of the following precautions: do not use masses greater than a few hundred grams **(1)**, wear eye protection **(1)**, use electrically tested electronic equipment **(1)**, avoid trailing electrical leads **(1)**.

70 Newton's third law

1. For every action there is an equal and opposite reaction **(1)**.

2. As the rocket sits on the launch pad, its weight downwards is equal and opposite to **(1)** the reaction force upwards of the launch pad **(1)**, so the rocket does not fall through.

3. The weight of the penguin is pushing down on the ice and the reaction force of the ice is pushing back on the penguin **(1)**, so the penguin is supported by the ice and does not fall through **(1)**.

4. Newton's third law says that the forces must be equal in size / magnitude **(1)** and opposite **(1)** in direction to be in equilibrium. The force exerted by the buttresses on the building **(1)** is equal and opposite to the force exerted on the buttresses by the building **(1)** resulting in no movement occurring.

71 Stopping distance

1. (a) thinking distance + braking distance = overall stopping distance **(1)**

   (b) Thinking distance will increase if: the car's speed increases, the driver is distracted, the driver is tired, or the driver has taken alcohol or drugs **(1)**. (All four points needed for mark.)

   Braking distance will increase if: the car's speed increases, the road is icy or wet, the brakes or tyres are worn, or the mass of the car is bigger **(1)**. (All four points needed for mark.)

2. (a) Work done **(1)** by the friction force between the brakes and the wheel **(1)** reduces the kinetic energy of the vehicle **(1)**.

   (b) The temperature of the brakes increases because kinetic energy of the vehicle **(1)** is transferred to thermal energy by the brakes **(1)**.

3. Driving faster will increase thinking distance **(1)** and braking distance **(1)**. If drivers do not increase their normal distance behind the vehicle in front accordingly, there is an increased risk of an accident / collision **(1)**.

72 Reaction time

1. Overall stopping distance would be longer **(1)**.

2. Human reaction time is the time taken between a stimulus and a response **(1)**. It is related to how quickly the human brain can process information and react to it **(1)**.

3. (a) A person waits with his index finger and thumb opened to a gap of about 8 cm **(1)**. A metre ruler is held, by a partner, so that it is vertical and exactly level with the person's finger and thumb / with the lowest numbers on the ruler by the person's thumb **(1)**. The ruler is dropped and then grasped by the other person

as quickly as possible **(1)**. A reading of distance can then be taken from the ruler. **(1)**

   (b) 0.2 s to 0.9 s **(1)**

   (c) The distance measured on the ruler would be short for the person with a reaction time of 0.2 s **(1)** and longer for the person with a reaction time of 0.9 s **(1)**.

73 Extended response – Forces

The answer should include some of the following points: **(6)**

- As the skydiver jumps from the plane, weight / force acts in a downward direction.
- The upward / resistive force is caused by air resistance acting on the skydiver.
- The downward and upward forces act in opposite directions to give a resultant force.
- The resultant force is downwards / causing the skydiver to accelerate.
- The 'spread-out' position of the skydiver increases the surface area exposed to the air resistance, increasing the upward force and reducing the rate of acceleration.
- Maximum velocity occurs when the downward and upward forces are in balance.
- The parachute increases air resistance, increasing the upward force.
- Increased upwards force causes the skydiver to decelerate.
- When the skydiver and parachute have slowed to a velocity where the upwards and downwards forces are again balanced, the skydiver falls to the ground at a slower terminal velocity.

74 Waves

1. When energy travels through water, we can see that the water particles themselves do not travel. This is because an object on the surface will 'bob' up and down / vertically **(1)** as the wave passes horizontally **(1)**.

2. The vibrations in a longitudinal wave are in the same direction as the wave is travelling / energy transfer **(1)**. The vibrations in a transverse wave are at right angles to the direction the wave is travelling / energy transfer **(1)**.

3. (a) 0.025 m **(1)**

   (b) 12 cm / 2 (as there are 2 waves shown) so wavelength = 6 cm = 0.06 **(1)** m

   (c) any correct wave with higher amplitude (height) **(1)** and shorter wavelength **(1)**

   (d) To find frequency use $v = f\lambda$, so $f = 3 \times 10^8$ m/s / 0.12 m **(1)** $= 2 \times 10^9$ Hz **(1)** (or 2 $\times 10^6$ kHz / 2500 MHz / 2.5 GHz)

   To find time period use $period = 1 / frequency$ so $period = 1 / 2 \times 10^9$ **(1)** (allow error carried forward from finding frequency) $= 5 \times 10^{-10}$ seconds / s **(1)**

75 Wave equation

1. Wave speed = 0.017 m × 20 000 Hz **(1)** = 340 **(1)** m/s

2. (a) $v = f\lambda$ rearranged is $f = v / \lambda$, so $f = 1500$ m/s / 88 m **(1)** = 17 **(1)** Hz

   (b) $\lambda = v / f$ so $\lambda = 1500$ m/s / 22 Hz **(1)** = 68.2 m **(1)**

3. $\lambda = v / f = 0.05$ m/s / 2 Hz **(1)** = 0.025 **(1)** m **(1)**

76 Measuring wave velocity

1. Frequency (f) = 3 Hz, wavelength (λ) = 0.05 m, speed of waves = 3 Hz × 0.05 m **(1)** = 0.15 **(1)** m/s **(1)**

2. 8 m **(1)**

3. T = 4 divisions × 0.005 ms = 0.02 s **(1)** $period = 1 / frequency$ so $period = 1 / 0.02$ s **(1)** = 50 **(1)** Hz

77 Required practical – Waves in fluids

1. (a) Count the number of waves that pass a point each second and do this for one minute (or any suitable time interval) **(1)**; divide the total by 60 to get a more accurate value for the frequency of the water waves **(1)**.

   (b) Use a stroboscope to 'freeze' the waves **(1)** and find their wavelength by using a ruler in the tank/on a projection **(1)**.

   (c) wave speed = frequency × wavelength or $v = f \times \lambda$ **(1)**

   (d) the depth of the water **(1)**

2. A ripple tank can be used to determine a value for the wavelength, frequency and wave speed of water waves **(1)** as long as small wavelengths **(1)** and small frequencies are used **(1)**.

3. water: hazard – spills may cause slippages; safety measure – report and wipe up immediately **(1)**; electricity: hazard – may cause shock or trailing cables; safety measure – do not touch plugs / wires / switches with wet hands or keep cables tidy **(1)**; strobe lamp: hazard – flashing lights may cause dizziness or fits; safety measure – check that those present are not affected by flashing lights **(1)**

78 Waves and boundaries

1. (a) smooth stone wall **(1)**

   (b) Stone is more dense **(1)** and, the greater the difference in density between materials, the more sound energy will be reflected **(1)**.

2. Light waves from an object on the surface are reflected at a plane surface **(1)**. The angle of incidence equals the angle of reflection **(1)** when measured against a normal drawn perpendicular to the plane surface **(1)**. (Both required for mark.) This is repeated at the bottom of the periscope so that the light reaches the user **(1)** (or similar wording).

3. normal shown and labelled **(1)**; incident and reflected rays shown and labelled **(1)**; angle of incidence = angle of reflection **(1)**

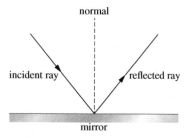

79 Required practical – Investigating refraction

1. (a) Place a refraction block on white paper and connect a ray box to an electricity

supply **(1)**; switch on the ray box and set it at an angle to the surface of the block **(1)**; use a sharp pencil to draw around the refraction block and make dots down the centre of the rays either side of the block **(1)**; use a sharp pencil and ruler to join the 'external' rays and then draw a line across the outline of the block to join the lines **(1)**; use a protractor to draw a normal where the light ray met the block and measure the angle of incidence and angle of refraction **(1)**.

(b) When a light ray travels from air into a glass block, its direction changes **(1)** and the angle of refraction will be less than the angle of incidence **(1)**.

(c) (i) The ray of light would not change direction **(1)**.

(ii) The light would slow down **(1)** (travelling from a less dense medium to a more dense medium) and the wave fronts would be closer together / the wavelength of light would be shorter **(1)**.

2 any three from: use of electricity: if mains electricity is used there is a risk of shock – use tested apparatus / do not try to plug in / unplug in the dark **(1)**; experiments are generally done in low-level light so there is a risk of tripping – clear floor area and working space (no trailing wires) and avoid moving around too much **(1)**; if glass blocks are used there is a risk of cuts – handle with care, use Perspex / non-breakable blocks when possible **(1)**; ray boxes get hot so risk of burns – do not touch ray boxes during operation **(1)**

3 The waves travel more slowly and wavelength becomes shorter in shallow water **(1)**; the waves change direction / bend towards the 'normal' as they move into shallower water **(1)**.

80 Electromagnetic spectrum

1 (a) All waves of the electromagnetic spectrum are transverse waves **(1)** and they all travel at 3×10^8 m/s / the same speed in a vacuum **(1)**.

(b) Any suitable example, e.g. transmission of radio and TV signals using radio waves, use of microwaves to transfer information to and from mobile phones **(1)**.

2 (a) A: X-rays **(1)**
B: visible light **(1)**
C: microwaves **(1)**

(b) Frequency increases from radio waves to gamma-rays **(1)**. The energy of the radiation increases with frequency **(1)**, so gamma-rays have the most energy and radio waves the least **(1)**.

3 $v = f\lambda$, so $f = v / \lambda = 3 \times 10^8$ m/s / 240 m **(1)** $= 1.25 \times 10^6$ **(1)** Hz

81 Required practical – Infrared radiation

1 (a) any four from: Fill Leslie's cube with hot water at a known temperature (e.g. wait until it falls to 80 °C before taking temperature measurements) **(1)**. Measure the temperature at a distance (e.g. 10 cm) **(1)** from one of the four sides of Leslie's

cube for a period of time (e.g. 5 minutes) **(1)**. Take regular readings (e.g. every 30 seconds) **(1)**. Repeat method for the other three sides **(1)**.

(b) The dependent variable is temperature **(1)**. The independent variable is the sides of the Leslie's Cube **(1)**.

(c) Any four from: starting temperature of the water, distance of heat sensor/thermometer from the cube, length of time, same number of readings taken, same intervals of time for each temperature reading, use the same thermometer or temperature sensor. All four correct for **2 marks**; three correct for **1 mark**; two or fewer correct for **0 marks**.

2 (a) and (b) Any one hazard and method of minimising it from: Hot water in eyes can cause damage **(1)** – always wear eye protection **(1)**. Boiling water can cause scalds **(1)** – place the kettle close to cube and fill the cube in its place **(1)**. The cube can cause burns **(1)** – do not touch the cube until the temperature reading is low **(1)**. Water and electricity can result in a shock **(1)** – when using an electrical temperature sensor, keep well away from water **(1)**. Trailing wires can be a trip hazard **(1)** – avoid trailing leads / tuck leads out of the way **(1)**.

3 (a) The bungs would minimise thermal energy transferred from the flasks through evaporation **(1)**.

(b) (i) Dull and black surfaces are the best emitters and best absorbers **(1)**.

(ii) Shiny and light surfaces are the worst emitters and worst absorbers **(1)**.

82 Dangers and uses

1 (a) Infrared waves: (any **two** from) night vision goggles / security sensor / TV remote control / cooking / thermal imaging camera **(1)**

(b) Ultraviolet waves: (any **two** from) disinfecting water / sterilising surgical / scientific instruments / entertainment lighting / security marking **(1)**

(c) Gamma-rays: (any **two** from) sterilising food / treating cancer / detection of cracks (pipes / aircraft, etc.) **(1)**

(d) Communication / mobile phones / satellites **(1)**

2 (a) The oral X-ray delivers the least amount of radiation, 0.005 mSv, which is the same as 1 day's normal exposure to background radiation. The next highest dose is for a chest X-ray which delivers 0.1 mSv, equivalent to 10 days of background radiation, and the highest dose is for the lung cancer screening, which delivers 1.5 mSv, equivalent to 6 months' exposure to background radiation. (X-rays in the right order, **(1)** dose related to equivalent background radiation for all three, **(1)** data quoted from table for all three **(1)**))

(b) If a person has too many X-rays in a certain time, particularly higher-dose X-rays, they may be more at risk of damage to body cells **(1)** if the X-rays are

not carefully controlled to allow the body to recover from the high-energy doses **(1)**.

3 Ultraviolet radiation can cause skin to age prematurely **(1)**. It can also increase the risk of skin cancer **(1)**.

83 Lenses

1 A converging lens bends the rays of light towards each other **(1)**. A diverging lens bends the rays of light away from each other **(1)**.

2 (a) Thick lens: mid-ray continues unchanged; top and bottom rays angle down steeply **(1)**, focal point relatively close to the lens **(1)**.

Thin lens: mid-ray continues unchanged; top and bottom rays angle down less steeply than for lens 1 **(1)**, focal point further from lens **(1)**.

(b) convex lens **(1)**

3 (a) Three construction rays **(1)**, divergent rays extrapolated **(1)**, focal point correctly identified **(1)**, focal length correctly labelled **(1)**.

focal length (f)

focal point (F)

(b) (i) Virtual **(1)**

(ii) Concave lenses only form virtual images **(1)** because the rays diverge / are extrapolated by the brain of the observer **(1)**.

4 (a) If the lens is thicker, the focal point will be closer to the lens / a shorter distance from the lens **(1)**. If the lens is thinner, the focal point will be further away from the lens / a longer distance from the lens **(1)**.

(b) The focal length is the distance from the lens to the principal focus **(1)**.

84 Real and virtual images

1 A real image is an image that can be projected on a screen **(1)** but a virtual image cannot be projected on a screen **(1)**. A virtual image is produced when light rays appear to come from a point beyond the object **(1)**.

2 (a) points added at the distance 2F on both sides of the lens **(1)**

(b) point added at the same distance as F on the right-hand side of the lens **(1)**

(c) vertical arrow drawn from where the two rays of light cross on the right-hand side up to the central line **(1)**

3 Image height = magnification × object height, so image height = 4.5 × 3.3 **(1)** = 14.85 mm **(1)**

4 (a) The magnification of the image increases **(1)**.

(b) when the object is closer to the lens than the focal point **(1)**

(c) at 2F **(1)**

85 Visible light

1 translucent and transparent **(1)**

2 any plane surface such as a mirror, very smooth water, polished glass **(1)**

3 An opaque green object appears green because it reflects green light (1) and all other colours are absorbed (1).

4 (a) Violet light has a shorter wavelength than red light (1) so it carries more energy.

(b) Yellow light is a combination of red light and green light (1). The green book cover absorbs red wavelengths of light but reflects green wavelengths of light, so it still looks green (1). The blue title absorbs both red and green wavelengths of light and so looks black (1).

5

Diagram must show: Incident rays all parallel, reflected rays reflected in different directions (1). Uneven surface shown to represent rough surface (1).

The following points are acceptable as description only or as shown on the diagram: Diffuse reflection still obeys the law of reflection because each ray of light that arrives at a surface is still reflected (1) according to the law of reflection (angle i = angle r) (1). At the microscopic level, the surface is not smooth / the microscopic surfaces are at different angles to each other (1).

86 Black body radiation

1 The cup emits more radiation than it absorbs (1).

2 Cup A will radiate more heat in 5 minutes (1) because the hotter the body the more infrared radiation it radiates in a given time (1).

3 A perfect black body is an object that absorbs all of the radiation incident on it (1). A black body does not reflect or transmit any radiation (1). Since a good absorber is also a good emitter, a perfect black body would be the best possible emitter (1).

4 Astronomers measure intensity of wavelengths of the light from a star to determine the peak / main wavelength (1); they can then relate this to a scale of wavelength emitted at certain temperatures and so determine the temperature of the star (1) (or similar wording).

87 Extended response – Waves

The answer should include some of the following points: (6)

- X-rays and gamma-rays are both transverse waves.
- X-rays and gamma-rays have a high frequency and therefore carry high amounts of energy.
- X-rays and gamma-rays cause ionisation in atoms and exposure can be dangerous / cause cells to become cancerous.
- People who work regularly with X-rays and gamma-rays should limit their exposure by using shields or leaving the room during use.
- X-rays are transmitted by normal body tissue but are absorbed by bones and other dense materials such as metals.

- X-rays and gamma-rays mostly pass through body tissue but can be absorbed by some types of cells such as bone.
- X-rays and gamma-rays can be used to investigate / treat medical problems.
- X-rays and gamma-rays are used in industry to examine / 'see' into objects to examine for cracks / failures.

88 Magnets and magnetic fields

1 field lines **out** (arrows) of N (1), field lines **in** (arrows) at S (1), field line close at poles (1), further apart at sides (1)

2 A bar magnet and the Earth both have north and south poles (1). A bar magnet and the Earth have similar magnetic field patterns (1). The direction of both fields can be found using a plotting compass (1).

3 An induced magnet is used for an electric doorbell because it can be magnetised when the current is switched on (1), which attracts the soft iron armature to ring the bell (1), and is de-magnetised when the current is switched off (1) (moving the armature away from the bell). An induced magnet is used as the 'switching' off and on of the magnet allows the arm to be moved and the bell rung (1). Also, the default 'rest' state of the bell does not need any energy input (1).

89 Current and magnetism

1 (a) at least two concentric circles on each diagram (2)

(b) clockwise arrows on cross diagram (1); anticlockwise arrows on dot diagram (1)

(c) by increasing the current (1)

2 (a) bar magnet (1)

(b) Insert an iron core into the solenoid (1).

3 The force acting on a current-carrying wire in a magnetic field depends on the length / l (1) of the wire, the current / I (1) in the wire and the magnetic flux density / B (1).

90 Extended response – Magnetism and electromagnetism

The answer should include some of the following points: (6)

- A long straight conductor could be connected to a cell, an ammeter and a small resistor to prevent overheating in the conductor.
- When the current is switched on the direction of the magnetic field generated around a long straight conductor can be found using the right-hand grip rule.
- The right-hand grip rule points the thumb in the direction of conventional current and the direction of the fingers shows the direction of the magnetic field.
- A card can be cut halfway through and placed at right angles to the long straight conductor. A plotting compass can be used to show the shape and direction of the magnetic field.
- The shape of the magnetic field around the long straight conductor will be circular /

concentric circles as the current flows through it.

- The strength of the magnetic field depends on the distance from the conductor.
- The concentric magnetic field lines mean that the field becomes weaker with increasing distance.
- The strength of the magnetic field can be increased by increasing the current.

91 The Solar System

1 Sun, planets, dwarf planets, moons (all required for mark) (1)

2 A planet orbits the Sun / a star (1) but a moon orbits a planet (1).

3 (a) The Solar System has only one star (1) but the Milky Way contains over one billion stars (1).

(b) The Solar System is a simple star system / has orbiting planets / is comparatively small (1) but the Milky Way is a spiral galaxy / collection of stars / contains planets **and** stars / is much bigger (accept any valid description of the Milky Way (accept any other valid difference) (1).

4 (a) 1. terrestrial / rocky planets (1)
2. gas giants (1)

(b) Saturn (1)

(c) Saturn is a gas giant whereas the other three planets are terrestrial / rocky planets (1).

(d) The Earth has a solid crust with a separate gaseous atmosphere / atmosphere was produced through geological processes (1) whereas the surface of Neptune is gaseous and there seems to be no definite boundary between the 'surface' and the 'atmosphere' (1).

(e) planet (1)

(f) dwarf planet (1)

92 The life cycle of stars

1 (nuclear) fusion (1)

2 gravity (1)

3 From top left to bottom right: protostar, supergiant, giant, supernova, white dwarf, neutron, hole, dwarf. All 8 correct: **4 marks**; 6 or 7 correct: **3 marks**; 4 or 5 correct: **2 marks**; 2 or 3 correct: **1 mark**; 0 or 1 correct: **0 marks**.

4 All of the naturally occurring elements in the periodic table are produced by fusion processes in stars (1). Elements heavier than iron (1) are produced in supernova explosions (1). These explosions of massive stars (1) then distribute the elements throughout the universe (1).

93 Satellites and orbits

1 natural satellites (1)

2 The orbit of a planet is around a star (accept the Sun) (1) whereas the orbit of a moon is around a planet (1).

3 (a) gravity (1)

(b) (i) geostationary orbit, low-polar orbit (1)

(ii) geostationary: any one of: global positioning systems (GPS) / satellite TV / communications (1); low-polar:

any one of: weather monitoring / military / spying / Earth observation **(1)**

4 (a) Planets, moons and artificial satellites all move in circular **(1)** orbits.

(b) A moon orbits at a fixed distance **(1)** from its planet but the orbit of an artificial satellite can be changed by adjusting its speed **(1)** and the radius of its orbit **(1)**.

94 Red-shift

1 The wavelength increases **(1)**.

2 A galaxy with a red-shifted spectrum indicates that the galaxy is moving away from the observer **(1)**. The further the black lines are shifted the faster it is moving away **(1)**. As most galaxies are red-shifted this would suggest that the universe is expanding **(1)**.

3 (a) the Big Bang theory **(1)**

(b) the observation of supernovae **(1)** in red-shift **(1)**

(c) This suggests that the universe began from one very small region **(1)** that was extremely dense (accept hot) **(1)**.

(d) (i) dark matter **(1)** and dark energy **(1)**

(ii) The universe is believed to be expanding even faster than was first thought **(1)**. There is much about the universe that we do not yet understand **(1)**.

95 Extended response – Space physics

The answer should include some of the following points: **(6)**

- The Big Bang theory states that the universe started from a very small, hot and dense space in a massive explosion about 13.8 billion years ago.
- The universe has been expanding and cooling ever since.
- The observed red-shift of light from galaxies provides evidence that the universe is expanding and supports the Big Bang Theory.
- There is an observed increase in the wavelength of light from most distant galaxies.
- The further away the galaxies are, the faster they are moving and the bigger the observed increase in wavelength. This effect is called red-shift.
- The observed red-shift provides evidence that space itself (the universe) is expanding and supports the Big Bang theory.
- Scientists were able to either repeat the same experiment or test the theory using another method so the Big Bang theory was accepted.
- Since 1998 onwards, observations of supernovae suggest that distant galaxies are receding ever faster so this may lead to a theory that replaces the Big Bang theory.
- If future experiments find a better explanation of the origin of the universe, then this theory will be adapted or replaced.

96 Timed Test 1

1 (a) (i) background radiation **(1)**

(ii) Any two from: radon gas, **(1)** cosmic rays **(1)**, medical uses **(1)**, nuclear industry **(1)**, natural sources / rocks **(1)**

(iii) Several readings are taken to identify anomalies to gain a reading close to the true value **(1)**.

(b) (i) y-axis labelled 'Corrected count rate (counts / min)' and x-axis labelled 'Time in minutes'; **(1)** all points plotted correctly (to within half a square) **(2)** [or six or more points correctly plotted (to within half a square) for 1 mark]

(ii) single exponential decay curve of best fit passing through six points **(1)**

(iii) half-life = 2 minutes **(1)**

(c) Alpha radiation is highly ionising because it is the most massive particle so it can easily ionise atoms by knocking off their electrons **(1)**. Beta radiation is moderately ionising; the particles are highly energised although very small so have less chance of knocking electrons off other atoms **(1)**. Gamma radiation is the least ionising because it has no mass but the gamma-rays may still ionise other atoms **(1)**.

2 (a) (i) $E_p = m\,g\,h$

Energy gained = 750 kg × 10 N/kg × 15 m **(1)** = 112 500 **(1)** J

(ii) Power $P = E_p / t$ = 112 500 J / 20 s **(1)** = 5625 **(1)** W **(1)**

(b) Any one of: thermal energy store of the motor **(1)**, thermal energy store of the elevator materials **(1)**, thermal energy store of the environment **(1)**, sound energy store **(1)**

(c) $v = d / t$ = 15 m / 20 s **(1)** = 0.75 m/s **(1)**

Kinetic energy, $E_k = \frac{1}{2}\,m\,v^2 = \frac{1}{2} × 750$ kg × $(0.75$ m/s$)^2$ **(1)** = 210.9 **(1)** J

(d) This process could be described as wasteful because it causes a rise in temperature in parts of the system **(1)** so dissipating energy in heating the surroundings **(1)**.

(e) a rise in temperature in any one of: the lift motor **(1)**, the fabric of the lift **(1)**, the lift cables **(1)**

3 (a) (i) $P = V\,I$ / power = voltage × current **(1)**

(ii) $I = P / V$ = 2000 W / 230 V **(1)** = 8.7 A **(1)**

(iii) Too high a fuse could result in too much current and the risk of a fire **(1)**; too low a fuse would melt and break the circuit each time the kettle was switched on **(1)**.

(iv) 10 A **(1)**

(b) 2000 W = 2000 J/s so E = 2000 J and $E = Q\,V$, so $Q = E / V$ = 2000 J / 230 **(1)** V = 8.7 **(1)** coulombs / C **(1)**

4 (a) Energy supplied $E = I\,V\,t$ = 12 A × 12 V × 120 s **(1)** = 17 280 **(1)** joules / J **(1)**

(b) $\Delta E = m\,c\,\Delta\theta$ so $\Delta\theta = \Delta E / (m\,c)$ = 17 280 J / (2 kg × 385 J/kg °C) **(1)**

Temperature change = 22.4 **(1)** degrees Celsius / °C **(1)**

(c) Some thermal energy is dissipated to the environment **(1)**.

(d) (i) by thermally insulating the block **(1)**

(ii) insulator **(1)**

5 (a) (i) $^{231}_{91}\mathrm{Pa} \rightarrow\, ^{227}_{89}\mathrm{Ac} + ^{4}_{2}\mathrm{He}$

i.e. 231, 89, 2 **(1)** (all three needed for mark)

(ii) alpha decay **(1)**

(b) (i) $^{211}_{87}\mathrm{Fr} \rightarrow\, ^{4}_{2}\mathrm{He} + ^{207}_{85}\mathrm{At}$

i.e. 211, 4, 85 **(1)** (all three needed for mark)

(ii) alpha decay **(1)**

(c) (i) $^{24}_{11}\mathrm{Na} \rightarrow\, ^{24}_{12}\mathrm{Mg} + ^{0}_{-1}\mathrm{e}$

i.e. 12, 0 **(1)** (both needed for mark)

(ii) beta decay **(1)**

(d) (i) $^{201}_{79}\mathrm{Au} \rightarrow\, ^{201}_{80}\mathrm{Hg} + ^{0}_{-1}\mathrm{e}$

i.e. 79, 201 **(1)** (both needed for mark)

(ii) beta decay **(1)**

(e) (i) Alpha decay causes both the mass and the charge of the nucleus to decrease **(1)**.

(ii) Beta decay does not cause the mass of the nucleus to change but does cause the charge of the nucleus to increase **(1)**.

6 (a) (i) As the fuel flows through the delivery pipe, electrons can build up due to friction **(1)** because the fuel pipe is made from an insulating material **(1)**.

(ii) The build-up of static charge on an insulator could result in a spark **(1)**. This would be dangerous because it could ignite the fuel / fumes / vapour **(1)**.

(b) The earth wire is made from a conducting metal **(1)** that allows electrons to flow away to earth to prevent them building up a static charge. **(1)**

(c) *The answer should include some of the following points:* **(6)**

- A charged object creates an electric field around itself.
- The electric field is strongest close to the charged object.
- The further away from the charged object, the weaker the field.
- A second charged object placed in the field experiences a force.
- The force gets stronger as the distance between the objects decreases.

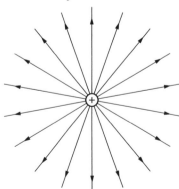

Diagram should include: positive point source, radial field lines, arrows outwards to show direction of field.

7 (a) Each lamp would have a potential difference of 0.5 V **(1)** because potential difference is shared in a series circuit **(1)**.

(b) voltmeter connected in parallel across one of the lamps **(1)**

(c) An additional cell could be added **(1)**.

115

Answers

(d) The lamps could be connected in a parallel circuit (1).

(e) (i) The resistance of a thermistor changes with temperature (1). When the temperature rises more electrons are released (1), causing more current to flow and reducing resistance (accept converse) (1).

(ii) used in a temperature-sensing circuit (1)

8 (a) solid – closely packed particles in fixed positions within a regular lattice

liquid – closely packed particles, irregular arrangement

gas – few particles, spread out in random arrangement (all three correct, (2) two correct (1))

(b) *The answer should include some of the following points:* (6)

- Particles in a solid have a relatively low amount of kinetic energy compared with the other states of matter
  o and remain in molecular bonding with neighbouring atoms.
- Particles in a liquid have higher amounts of kinetic energy than solids
  o but lower amounts of kinetic energy than gases
  o and remain in weak molecular bonding with / can move around neighbouring atoms.
- Particles in a gas have a high amount of kinetic energy
  o and can move independently of other neighbouring atoms.

9 (a) $\rho_1 = m / V = 1.5$ kg $/ 0.2$ m$^3 = 7.5$ kg/m^3 (1)

$\rho_2 = 0.7$ kg $/ 0.15$ m$^3 = 4.7$ kg/m^3 (1)

$\rho_3 = 0.7$ kg $/ 0.2$ m$^3 = 3.5$ kg/m^3 (1)

so block 1 has the highest density (1)

(b) (i) The student must make sure that the line of sight from the eye to the meniscus (1) is perpendicular to the scale (1) (to avoid parallax errors).

(ii) The student must measure the mass of the rock (1). This can be done on a balance or hung from a suspended force meter (1).

10 (a) Thomson's 'plum pudding' model referred to the atom as a positively charged sphere (1) with negative charges / electrons distributed throughout the sphere (1). Rutherford's nuclear model of the atom showed the positive charges concentrated in a tiny nucleus (1) with the negative charges / electrons orbiting around the outside of the nucleus (1).

(b) *The answer should include some of the following points:* (6)

- Alpha particles directed at gold foil
- Most alpha particles pass straight through
  o so most of the atom is empty space.
- A few alpha particles deflected through large angles
- Mass is concentrated at the centre of the atom
  o so the nucleus must be tiny.
- Nucleus is (positively) charged

o so the negative charges orbit around the dense positive nucleus.

100 Timed Test 2

1 (a) Measure, mark and record the distance to be travelled by the trolley (1), place the trolley at the start / top of the ramp and release (1), time how long it takes to cover the marked distance (1) (both distance and timing should be mentioned for the mark). Repeat the experiment to reduce the influence of random errors (1).

(b) any two from: light gates (1), data logger (1), computer (1)

(c) (i) independent variable: height (1)

(ii) column 1: Height (of ramp); column 2: Distance (travelled by trolley); column 3: Time (1) (all needed for mark)

(iii) Speed (m/s) (1)

(d) (i) Friction between the wheels and the surface / floor and axles (1); air resistance (1).

(ii) Friction could be reduced by (any one of the following): using a smoother surface on the ramp / smoother surface on the wheels / lubricating the axles (1). Air resistance could be reduced by (any one of the following): making the trolley more aerodynamic / reducing the surface area of the front of the trolley (1).

2 (a) change in velocity (accept initial and final velocity) (1), time (1)

(b) $a = \Delta v / t = 10 / 20$ (1) $= 0.5$ (1) m/s^2

(c) $(v^2 - u^2) = 2 a s$, so $s = (v^2 - u^2) / 2 a$ (1) $= 100 / 2 \times 0.5$ (1) $= 100$ (1) m

3 (a) supernova (1)

(b) (i) Nuclear fusion is the joining of two light nuclei to form a heavier nucleus (1).

(ii) Fusion processes in stars produce all the naturally occurring elements (1). Fusion processes lead to the formation of new elements (1).

(iii) Elements heavier than iron are produced in a supernova (1). The explosion of a massive star (supernova) distributes the elements throughout the universe (1).

4 (a) (i) time period = 1 / frequency or $T = 1 / f$ (1)

(ii) 'T' should be marked between the start and end of an identified single wave cycle (1).

(iii) First find T so T = 0.0001 / 2 (2 waves shown) so T = 0.00005 (1) so T = 1 / 0.000 05 s (1) = 20 000 (1) Hz

(b) (i) The amplitude of a wave is the maximum displacement of a point on a wave away from its undisturbed position (1).

(ii) The wavelength of a wave is the distance from a point on one wave to the equivalent point on the adjacent wave (1).

(iii) The frequency of a wave is the number of waves passing a point each second (1).

(c) transverse and longitudinal (1) (both needed for mark)

5 (a) reflection (1)

(b) (i) *i* marked between incident ray and normal (1), *r* marked between normal and refracted ray (inside the block) (1)

(ii) The 'normal' is a line drawn perpendicular / at right angles / at 90° to the surface of a transparent or translucent material on a ray diagram. (1) The angle between the normal and light ray is the angle of incidence / refraction. (1)

(c) Rays drawn – tip of object to mid-lens then down through F$_2$ (1). Second ray from tip of object through centre of lens to meet first ray (1). Position of image shown (1).

6 (a) A light source that is red-shifted will have a greater wavelength (1) and a lower frequency (1).

(b) The further away the galaxies, the faster they are moving (1) and the bigger the observed increase in wavelength (1).

(c) Red-shift provides evidence of an expanding universe (1), which supports the Big Bang model (1).

(d) Since 1998 onwards, observations of supernovae (1) have been recorded and suggest that the distant galaxies (1) in which they exist are receding at an even faster rate over time. (1)

(e) CMB radiation / cosmic microwave background radiation (1) which is detected from everywhere (1).

(f) • Scientists think that galaxies would rotate much faster if the stars they can see and detect were the only matter in galaxies. (1)
- Scientists have therefore proposed that there must be matter that cannot be detected or seen. (1)
- The concepts of dark mass and dark energy are not yet understood, but one day may account for the 'missing matter'. (1)

7 (a) gravity (1)

(b) Planets and dwarf planets orbit round the Sun (1) but moons orbit round planets (1).

(c) Jupiter is much larger than Mars / Jupiter is the largest planet in the Solar System (1). Jupiter has many more moons than Mars / Jupiter has over 50 confirmed moons whereas Mars has 2 (1).

(d) The circular path means a continual change of direction (1) and direction is a component of velocity (1).

(e) *The answer should include some of the following points:* (6)

- At the start of a star's life cycle, the dust and gas / nebula are drawn together by gravity.
- This causes fusion reactions.

- The fusion reactions lead to an equilibrium between:
  - the gravitational collapse of a star and
  - the expansion of a star due to fusion energy.
- As the star loses mass, it expands to become a red giant.
- The red giant then cools and collapses to become a white dwarf.

8 (a) (i) At least three arrows drawn **(1)** all arrows pointing clockwise around the wire **(1)**.

   (ii) the right-hand rule **(1)**

   (b) (i)

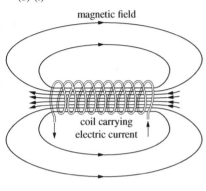

magnetic field

coil carrying electric current

   correct shape **(1)**, lines of flux very close inside **(1)**, lines of flux further apart outside **(1)**, pattern indicated on both sides of electromagnet **(1)**

   (ii) any valid use, e.g. doorbell, speaker, electromagnet **(1)**

   (c) The iron core increases the strength of the magnet **(1)**. As the iron core is a temporary magnet, the magnetic material can be released when the electromagnet is turned off **(1)**.

9 (a) (i) microwaves: communication / cooking / satellite transmission **(1)**

   (ii) ultraviolet: security marking / disinfecting water / detecting forged bank notes / fluorescent lamps **(1)**

   (iii) gamma-rays: detecting cancer/ treating cancer / sterilising food / medical equipment **(1)**

   (b) (i) transverse **(1)**

   (ii) All EM waves travel at the speed of light / 3×10^8 m/s in a vacuum **(1)**. All EM waves transfer energy **(1)**.

   (c) (i) diffuse reflection **(1)**

   (ii) The jumper reflects red light **(1)** and absorbs all the other colours **(1)**.

   (iii) The jumper absorbs the blue light **(1)** so no light is reflected and it would look black **(1)**.

10 (a) The students have not unloaded the spring each time to check that the deformation is elastic **(1)**.

   (b) The students should use the same masses to get more reliable results to show a proportional relationship **(1)**; they should unload the spring after measuring each extension to check that the deformation is still elastic **(1)**.

   (c) Missing values are, from top to bottom 36, 0.2, 44, 0.5 (all four correct **(2)**; three correct **(1)**)

   (d) In linear elastic deformation, the extension (of a spring) is directly proportional to the force added **(1)**. The graph is a straight line which shows a directly proportional relationship **(1)**. The spring is loaded with weights of 0.1 N at a time **(1)** and the spring extends by 4 mm with each 0.1 N **(1)**.

Physics Equation Sheet

(final velocity)^2 − (initial velocity)^2 = 2 × acceleration × distance	$v^2 - u^2 = 2\,a\,s$
elastic potential energy = 0.5 × spring constant × (extension)^2	$E_e = \dfrac{1}{2}\,k\,e^2$
change in thermal energy = mass × specific heat capacity × temperature change	$\Delta E = m\,c\,\Delta\theta$
period = $\dfrac{1}{\text{frequency}}$	
magnification = $\dfrac{\text{image height}}{\text{object height}}$	
thermal energy for a change of state = mass × specific latent heat	$E = m\,L$
for gases: pressure × volume = constant	$p\,V = constant$